C000245379

TED ELLIS

A Tapestry of Nature

Eastern Daily Press

When sorting through Ted's numerous cardboard boxes of papers following his death in July 1986, I found one box labelled "The Tapestry of Nature". This contained selected articles he intended to use in a book of that name. Ten years later, Percy Trett agreed to bind them together – an heroic task, and here is the book, possibly in a different format, but who can tell? So much help has been given to prepare this, Ted's work, for publication, and I can only offer my grateful thanks to:

Percy Trett, for re-typing all the original articles – a mammoth task.
Pete Kelley, who corrected, and Chris Blenkiron, who re-edited these pages.
Dr Roy Baker, for overseeing the Latin names and pictures.
Ruth Barnes, for permission to use the earlier drawings.
And many thanks to Sir Timothy for once more writing an introduction.
I am also so pleased that Eastern Counties Newspapers has decided to cope with the layout and publication on behalf of the Ted Ellis Trust.

Phyllis M Ellis MBE

ISBN 0-9502952-6-4

Front cover illustration by Dennis Whitehead
Produced by David Wakefield
An Eastern Daily Press Classics production

Introduction

April 1998

"In the opinion of the Councils of the Norfolk Naturalists Trust and the Norfolk and Norwich Naturalists Society, Dr Ted Ellis's contribution to our knowledge of the natural history of Norfolk is unique, and his example to existing and future generations of Norfolk people beyond praise."

This concluding sentence from the citation to his award of the Sydney Long Memorial Medal in 1986 sums up the reason and justification for this book.

Eugene Stone's delightful biography of Ted in 1988 was received with deserved acclaim. It projected, skilfully, a remarkable personality who combined meticulous observation and research with unassuming charm, and an exceptional gift for communicating with disciples of all ages.

There was only one conceivable regret about the biography – that it could not include more of Ted's writings. Hence this new volume, Tapestry of Nature, an accumulation of these articles which I am sure will engender renewed delight especially in these times of growing environmental enlightenment.

Who can fail to be tempted by a dip into this encyclopaedia of the natural world, a reminder that the miracles of nature are far more interesting than our own lives.

Equally gratifying for all who remember Ted is the fact that Wheatfen Broad, the subject of his life's devotion, today prospers as an International Ramsar site, and is in the safe hands of the Ted Ellis Trust, of which his widow, Phyllis, has been and remains the moving light.

Timothy Colman

Contents

Luminous Sea

Reedham Bridge 20/7/57

It is not necessary to visit the Tropics in order to see the ocean aglow at night with phosphorescent creatures. Here, on our North Sea coast, the waves sparkle with the golden flecks of Noctiluca as they break on the beach, and the sea lapping about the piers at our coast resorts is electrical with tiny flashes.

One dark and peaceful night in July a few years ago I rowed a punt down the river from Brundall to Yarmouth and, as I slipped through the Reedham Bridge, the punt seemed to run into a sheet of liquid fire.

The whole surface of the river down as far as Breydon was brilliantly phosphorescent; my oars were gilded every time they were dipped and rippled fire streamed from the punt's bows. On the estuary, the sparkles were more scattered by wind and racing tide, but the base of every post marking the main channel glittered where the ebbing current swirled by.

Noctiluca miliaris, the tiny marine organism responsible for this phosphorescence, is a flagellate animal about the size of a pin's head. It is easily discernible swimming, or rather floating, in a jar of seawater even in daylight. Under the microscope one can see it has a round body, in outline like a miniature water lily leaf, but inflated and translucent with little threads protruding from the groove where the leaf-lobes overlap.

As it drifts on the surface of the sea, Noctiluca catches even smaller creatures of the plankton, such as minute crustacea and the microscopic plants known as diatoms. There are many other luminous animals in the sea, including jellyfishes, hydroids, prawns and deep-water fish. In some instances, the lights produced are known to act as lures for intended prey, but no-one seems to have suggested that this might be the function of Noctiluca's flashing lamp. It is just possible that when the sea's surface is glittering with millions of tiny night-lights, the creatures forming the food of the torch-bearers are attracted to the surface.

There are no luminous organisms comparable with Noctiluca in the freshwaters of our rivers and pools, but it is not beyond the bounds of possibility that some freshwater crustacea are capable of producing phosphorescence at night in the muddy depths. On land, of course, we have glow-worms and luminous centipedes. These do not use their chemically-activated lamps as lures for prey. Glow-worms can emit light throughout life, from the egg state onwards, but it is developed most powerfully by the adult females which use their glowing beacons to attract the flying males. In luminous centipedes, the light-producing substance is of a liquid nature, and is used to spread confusion when the animal is attacked by an enemy in the darkness

Clam Once Relished in Norfolk

North West Norfolk 15/2/58

The delectable, soft-shelled clam so greatly prized in the USA, where it is the subject of a vast and carefully regulated fishery, has from time immemorial been a native of our North Sea coast. This shell-fish, known as the Gaper or Old Maid (*Mya arenaria*) abounds in the tidal sandy muds of the Wash, in Breydon Water, and all the Suffolk estuaries, where it burrows to a depth of up to a foot.

Although digging for clams at low tide is a fairly strenuous occupation, the molluscs can be depended on not to attempt escape by burrowing more deeply while the operation is in progress; they are not like lug-worms or razor shells in this respect.

Some 300 years ago, according to Sir Thomas Browne, they were relished by the inhabitants of Norfolk along with cockles, mussels and oysters. This tradition has not died out wholly at Lynn, I understand, but Breydon clams and those of the Suffolk coast seem to have been ignored by local fishermen for generations, even for use as bait.

Yet this same shell-fish is an article of food in other North European countries, and in China, as well as on both the Atlantic and Pacific coasts of North America. Possibly its neglect here may be due to the fact that more often than not we find it living in foul black mud, which is suggestive of unwholesomeness in the creature itself.

The clams of North-West Norfolk are large of their kind with the oblong shells measuring up to 6 x 3 inches. The outside is naturally greyish, but often stained rusty yellow or dark blue by the mud. The living animal has long siphons extending from one gaping end and these are sheathed by a wrinkled horny skin. When quite young, the clams just plough the surface and possess little beards, like mussels, for attaching themselves temporarily in order to withstand the force of tidal currents. They discard their beards once they have begun to burrow seriously.

The siphons are short at first, but continue to elongate as the molluscs grow larger and burrow more deeply, until they attain a length of as much as a foot. The siphon-mouth is fringed with little tentacles, which help to prevent coarse material from being drawn in. The mollusc's food consists of microscopically small creatures of the plankton.

When the clams die, their shells usually remain embedded vertically in the mud, but the horny siphon sheaths are washed away and are often found thrown ashore by the waves.

Mya arenaria is a creature of Northern waters and it has advanced southward and retreated with the coming and going of ice ages. It is a fossil of the shell beds in the Mediterranean, but lives in that sea no longer. Nearer home, we find it most anciently in the Red Crags of Suffolk, so we may say that it has been in these parts off and on for close on a million years.

Not Always Right-Handed

North Norfolk Coast 18/2/69

The "buckie" or almond whelk (**Neptunea antiqua**) occurs with common whelks in some of the deeper channels off the North Norfolk coast, though in relatively small numbers. Its solid white shells, tinged pink at the mouth, may often be seen washed ashore between Blakeney and Hunstanton.

The largest specimens seen in this part of the North Sea are a little over four inches long, although in deeper waters farther north they can attain a length of eight inches on occasion and Scottish and Hebridean fishermen have used them in the past as lamps when filled with oil and supplied with wicks hung in their homes.

Nowadays, with very rare exceptions, the shells of these whelks in coastal waters of Britain, the North Atlantic and Baltic have a right-handed spiral twist, like most ordinary whelks and the majority of winkle-like molluscs and land snails. This was not always so. In the early Pleistocene crags of East Anglia and especially in the Red Crag beds of Suffolk, the plentiful shells of *N. antiqua* have a left-handed twist, while normal specimens are relatively uncommon. Other shell fossil deposits in Britain and elsewhere in Northern Europe provide good evidence to show that the left-handed form was dominant over a wide sea area something over half a million years ago.

Since a succession of ice ages has affected this northern region, the right-handed form has become the normal type present, but the reversed form is still common in the warmer waters of the Mediterranean, as it was in Crag times, in that region as well as in Britain. Reversed shells are found in ordinary whelks caught off the Norfolk coast, but in very small numbers year by year. If such specimens were to be segregated in a marine aquarium the laws of heredity suggest that a pure race of left-handed whelks would materialise.

It has probably been a matter of chance that after glaciation wiped out our left-handed "buckies", those remaining in their haunts at the end of the great freeze happened to be right-handed and so came to achieve dominance. I know of no evidence indicating that whelk's eggs can be made to produce left-handed molluscs simply by placing them in warmer waters.

The almond whelk - *Neptunea antiqua*

9

Fossil sea urchin *Echinocorys scutatus*

Urchins Swarmed in the Sea Millions of Years Ago

King's Lynn 3/3/55

No-one believes in "fairy loaves" today, but all the same, the discovery of a five-rayed urchin-stone on a flint-strewn field is usually exciting enough for the finder to pocket the curiosity and either hoard it amongst the household knick-knacks or take it along to a museum for identification.

The example pictured here is a flint cast of the inside of the shell of a fossil sea urchin named ***Echinocorys scutatus*** (the English translation of this could be "shield heart-urchin"). The more complete fossils found in chalk pits look a little different, with a jigsaw covering of little plates forming the actual shell. The upper chalk of Norfolk contains millions of these urchins, which must have swarmed in the sea hereabouts some 70 million years ago.

Geologists have taken a great interest in these particular fossils and those of other kinds of chalk sea urchins, because it has been found that changes in shell form can be traced in a series of specimens taken between the lowest (oldest) and uppermost (youngest) beds, revealing the course of their evolution over a period of several million years. In most of the specimens found both in the chalk and out of it, no prickly spines are present; but like the sea urchins of today, these ancient and extinct species were equipped with numerous spines, which must have come adrift after the animals died in the white ooze of the old Chalk Sea.

Once in a while we find the impression of an odd spine in a flint. More rarely, a spine is visible in the same flint which holds an urchin-cast and as a result of long, patient study it has been found possible to reconstruct the original appearance of several kinds of these beautiful marine creatures, in form, if not in colour.

How the urchins came to be changed into flint or rather replaced by flint is something of a chemical mystery. Flint is a form of silica, with various impurities included. It seems to have been formed through the slow gathering of the silica by a process akin to crystallisation underground, the substance being collected little by little in liquid or gel form round nuclei of silica crystals which were present in sponges and other marine creatures embodied in the chalk deposits. How the fossil urchins came to lie on the present surface of arable land is another story. Briefly, they were left there in the sludge of glaciers at the end of the Ice Age. The glaciers collected material from the land over which they advanced, and it was only natural that in these parts they should churn up the underlying chalk, with its flinty fossils. By now most of the glacier chalk has been washed away, leaving the stones behind.

Sand Stars

Norfolk 27/2/82

Scouring waves and strong tidal currents often dislodge a variety of sea-bed creatures and cause them to be thrown up during the autumn.

Conspicuous amongst these castaways from time to time are quantities of little sand-stars with disc-like bodies and five very slender arms.

No less than 11 species have been found present in Norfolk's offshore waters, but several of these tend to inhabit the deeper waters and rarely reach the tidemarks.

Some, known as brittle stars, shed their arms, oftimes in fragments, at the slightest touch, so it is very unlikely they would appear in recognisable form after a bashing by waves on the shore.

The sand-stars are less fragile and the two species illustrated, **Ophiura texturata**, with long, snaky arms and the smaller **Ophiura albida** sometimes appear in swarms with most of their rays intact.

When brought up in shrimp trawls their lashing arms remind one of the tentacles of so many miniature octopuses and the same agitation is apparent on occasions when the waves sweep them ashore alive.

Unlike the common starfish, which devours mussels and other bivalve molluscs, the sand-stars are not equipped with tube feet for gripping and manipulating large prey; instead, they trap microscopic organisms by exuding a gummy substance from their pores.

In some sandy and muddy hollows of the sea bed they dwell in vast swarms presenting a strange spectacle to a diver who sees thousands of little writhing arms ever jostling for position.

When alive, they appear rosy or tinted with mauve or violet, but become bleached on drying. Some of them become luminous when excited.

From geological evidence we know that these creatures have inhabited the world's seas for 600 million years, having achieved their basic form very early and remained content with efficiency ever since. Even the experimental modifications which resulted in the evolution of sea urchins took place many millions of years ago, and while many species have been succeeded by others in the course of time, as can be seen at various levels in our Norfolk chalk, no monstrous change in design has taken place.

So long as the oceans remain unpoisoned, they can confidently look forward to a comfortable future for aeons of time.

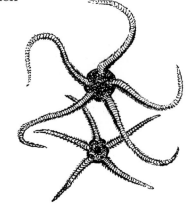

Sand Stars - *Ophiura albida and Ophiura textura*

Grotesquely Moulded Crabs

Happisburgh 7/9/57

To most people on our East Anglian coast a crab is one of two things: a Cromer crab or a sea Sammy, the latter being the all-too-common nuisance to fishermen in inshore waters, although found useful at times for bait. Yet several other kinds are present here and may be seen washed up at the tidemarks after storms.

Among these are some of the smaller species of spider crabs, often well camouflaged by seaweeds and other growths attached to their prickly carapaces, tiny pea-crabs living in mussels, hermit crabs living in winkle and whelk shells, brightly-coloured swimming crabs with velvet coats and paddles, little grey-toothed crabs from the "ross" grounds and strawberry crabs (so called from their strawberry mottlings) which dig themselves into the sand. Once in a while, we see the curious sponge-crab, from deeper water: a sluggish creature almost hidden by the sponges growing on its back.

One species which turns up on the beach occasionally and at once attracts attention is the masked crab, illustrated here. The back of its shell is moulded rather like a human face, grotseque as a mask. Males have long pincers and the females, short ones. They live only in comparatively clean sea sand, as a rule just below the limit of extreme low water at spring tides. I have found them at various times at points between Happisburgh and Lowestoft, but never on the Wash coast, where it seems likely that there is apt to be too much silt and clay for them.

They burrow backwards into the sand, the legs acting as scoops, until only the extreme tips of their antennae (feelers) remain showing above the surface. These feelers serve a very useful purpose. They are fringed with stiff little hairs, ranked in such a way that when the two sets are brought together they form a tube which excludes the sand and through which the crab draws a current of water for breathing. The gills are situated close to the mouth and work like a pump in reverse

The masked crabs are said to retire into the sand during the day and to come out and feed after dark. It is not necessary for their feelers to be joined in the form of a tube when they are wandering freely. Of course, it would be impracticable for them to burrow into clayey sand, because the bristles on their feelers are too coarse to strain out clay particles, which are exceedingly small.

These crabs have been found in the maws of North Sea cod and haddock fishes which commonly feed at the bottom of the sea and are capable of sucking out the crabs from the sand, just as they are of obtaining burrowing shellfish of other types. I do not know if they have any other living enemies, but their chief enemy must always be the mud brought down by rivers to the sea.

Lumpsucker's Six-Month Fast

Norfolk 5/7/58

One of the oddest fishes occurring in Norfolk's inshore waters is the lumpsucker, or "sea hen", a plump, gelatinous, flabby creature ornamented with stony knobs and equipped beneath with a large and powerful sucking disc by which it attaches itself to boulders on the sea bed. Small specimens are taken fairly commonly in shrimp nets; full-grown ones turn up more occasionally and most of those found are victims of rough weather in the winter and early spring when they are attempting to spawn in shallow water and are knocked about by the pounding waves.

The females grow to a length of two feet and are dark green and grey above and yellowish below; the males are smaller and more brightly coloured, having touches of blue and fiery orange-red bellies. The spawn, which is pink, is stuck in masses on seaweeds and stones round about low tide level and all the eggs, which may number more than 100,000, are laid in a single patch. The male fish, like the redbreast stickleback, broods over the eggs until they are hatched and uses his breast fins for fanning a constant stream of oxygenated water through the egg mass, to ensure that none shall die of suffocation.

Brooding males are seldom seen on our own coast, but in some places it is not uncommon for many of them to become uncovered periodically when the tides are out; they remain faithful to their charges, even though gulls and crows are apt to swoop upon them while they lie exposed. It is almost impossible to dislodge them when they are attached by their suckers to fixed rocks and it appears that, unlike nearly all other kinds of fishes, they are able to survive after laceration from the beaks of their attackers.

Lumpsuckers are not fished for deliberately in the sea round Britain, and their flesh is nowhere greatly esteemed, though the males, which have firmer flesh than the females, are eaten in some European countries to a small extent. When cooked, they become transformed into what Sir Thomas Browne 300 years ago described aptly as a "glutinous jelly". Fishermen have been known to boil them down with vegetables as food for pigs. The Norfolk zoologist J H Gurney snr observed that common seals preyed on lumpsuckers and took trouble to strip off the loose, knobbly skins before eating the bodies.

Anglers are familiar with freshwater fishes such as tench and carp which feed ravenously in the summer and fast for much of the winter. In lumpsuckers, this habit is reversed; the small crustaceans swarming in the sea in winter are consumed in large quantities. Then, from April onwards for a period of about six months, no food is taken and it seems that the fishes subsist on oil stored in their bodies. Infant lumpsuckers, although equipped with suckers early in life, swim about more actively than their parents and look rather like miniature tadpoles. Whenever one settles on a stone or a piece of seaweed it immediately curls its tail round its head and loses all resemblance to a fish.

Sting-Fish is a Hazard

East Anglian Coast 12/3/60

Shrimpers, longshoremen and bathers are only too painfully familiar with the lesser weever or sting-fish around the East Anglian coast. "Weever" in this instance is almost certainly a variant of the word "Viper". Sir Thomas Browne wrote it "Wiuer" and described how the sting-fish venomously pricked the hands of Norfolk fishermen.

Except for the sting ray, the greater and lesser weevers are the most dangerous fish in our local waters when they are being handled. They are armed with poison spines at the edges of their gill covers and on the back, the poison, secreted in specially infolded tissues, being injected forcibly into wounds made by the prickles. A Lowestoft surgeon, the late Dr Muir Evans, made a great study of this subject and found that the very painful and sometimes dangerous effects of the weever's poison required treatment in the same way as snake bites.

He also carried out experiments which showed that the presence of weever venom in the blood made it more difficult for a patient to battle with the germs most liable to get into wounds. This explains why it used to be common for weever stings to fester and prove difficult to heal before antibiotics became available. The venom itself produces some very nasty symptoms, which includes intense pain, swelling and inflamation. Breydon smelters used to say that the pain would not abate until the end of the next ebb tide after the prick, and not always as soon as that.

Lesser weever live in shallow inshore waters, where their food consists of shrimps which are engulfed as the fishes lie almost buried and well concealed in the sand. When approached by an enemy, the weever defends itself by lashing out with it poisoned daggers. This it does not only on the sea bed, but also when it has been taken out of the water.

Apart from the hazards experienced by fishermen and men sorting shrimps from their trawls, the chief risk is that bathers and children paddling at low tide may tread on a weever couched in the sand. The fish tends to lie with only its mouth, eyes and jet-black spiky back fin exposed.

Our common inshore species is usually little more than four inches long. Its back is a dirty sand colour, for camouflage, and the body is a pale yellow underneath. The Greater Weever grows to a length of a foot or a little more, is trawled from deeper water and is sometimes offered for sale in the shops. It possesses poison spines like its smaller relative and must be handled with great care. The larger fish can be distinguished from the smaller species when young by the presence of small spines over and beneath the eyes; the lesser weever lacks these. The sting of the Greater Weever has been known to cause the death of at least one trawler skipper.

Armour-Plated Nuisance

East Anglian Coast-17/2/70

Shrimpers and longshoremen of this region are all too familiar with a small armour-plated fish, a kind of bull-head or pogge, which in Norfolk is known as "hard-head" and in Suffolk, "beetle-head".

It abounds close inshore, working its way into estuaries and salt creeks during the summer months and at times it is a great nuisance, cluttering up the nets and trawls. Being of such an awkward shape, with rough ridges, upturned snout and large stiff fins, even very young specimens hang to the nets instead of slipping through the meshes and as a result, it is not uncommon for small specimens to get boiled with the shrimps and become objects of curious interest at tea tables.

In life, the pogge is a dirty-white colour peppered and marbled with grey, but when cooked it turns pink like a prawn. Needless to say, its exceedingly bony structure renders it unfit for eating and it is not used as bait.

Callous urchins playing down by the sea used to make sport with "hard-heads" by stuffing corks into their mouths and setting them adrift. In a primitive fashion one may suppose this sadistic operation on the part of fishermen's children was their way of showing how they despised these fish for their utter uselessness; it was akin to witch hunting.

Pogges deposit masses of pale yellow eggs on the rooting bases of the larger brown seaweeds in autumn and the fish then move into somewhat deeper water for the winter. The eggs have very hard shells and are said to withstand freezing while the fish themselves are able to flourish in Arctic waters.

A century ago, when there was much less pollution in our estuaries, spawn could be found encrusting mussels in the Wash and even occasionally in Breydon Water.

Pogge are especially abundant in the southern part of the North Sea and comparatively scarce in western parts of Britain. To a great extent their distribution must be affected by the trend of the currents, because the larvae have a habit of drifting helplessly at the surface for about three months after the eggs hatch.

The pogge - in Norfolk the hard-head, and in Suffolk, beetle-head.

Mullet Adept at Escaping

Breydon Water 10/4/71

A hundred years ago, grey mullet "rollicked in the sub-aqueous gardens" of Breydon Water, according to the recollections of my old mentor, A H Patterson.

In early boyhood he knew the Yarmouth estuary when its waters were a green paradise of sea-grass ribboning the clear shallows and there great shoals of silvery mullet were netted in season.

They used to nose their way in from the sea with some regularity in the early summer, working their way up the veined channels of the mudflats to feed in the more or less floating masses of sea-lettuce at high tide.

Fishermen often placed trammel nets in the drains to intercept them when the tides fell, but it was common for the mullet to escape by leaping like dolphins over the net. They are notoriously sagacious in this respect.

When I was a small boy I remember finding a "school" of mullet which had been marooned in a small tide-pool in one of Guernsey's sandy bays. I stood guard on the seaward side while my elder brother tried to secure the fish; but they jumped out one after another and skipped past me across a stretch of wet beach for a distance of something like fifty yards and made their escape into the sea.

At one time grey mullet used to swim up the Waveney and penetrate to Oulton Broad, where some of the villagers were in the habit of using barbed spears to secure them in shallow waters. H M Leathes believed that they actually bred at Oulton, but normally they spawn at the surface of the sea during the summer and enter estuaries mainly in search of food.

Patterson recorded that when barnacle-encrusted ships from the Mediterranean were docked for overhaul at Great Yarmouth in the old days, mullet sometimes followed them in and became stranded in the docks, the fish being attracted by the wealth of marine life on the ships' bottoms. Circumstances have changed and the mullet are now relatively scarce visitors to Breydon, although some still frequent our inshore waters in summer, along with salmon-trout.

Freshly caught grey mullet are delicious and to my mind almost as good as salmon-trout, but their flesh loses its firmness very quickly and the delicate flavour goes at the same time. Because of this, they have never been popular with fishmongers.

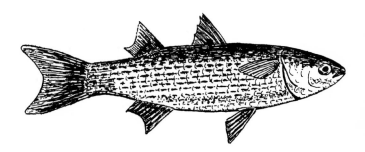

Gray mullet - now relatively scarce visitors to Breydon.

The Life of the Sea-Spider

Gorleston Breakwater 20/2/54

The gritty tangle of small feathery seaweeds and sand-coloured skeletons of corallines washed up in tenuous lines along our East Coast beaches only once in a while gives place to a richer spread of living jetsam, after storm waves and strong surges have torn the very bottom out of the offshore tide channels and wrenched matted chunks of the sea bed's blossoming wilderness from the even deeper ross-grounds.

On such occasions starfish may be flung ashore by the ton, with sorry whelks, miserably battered hermit crabs, violet and strawberry tinted sea-squirts patterned with golden stars, and thick, fleshy dahlia wartlet anemones which have lost most of their royal splendour in the bruising and tumbling they have undergone.

Then also one is likely to come upon an occasional sea-spider, a little stiff-jointed robot of an animal, invisibly yellow as it lies on the sand, but arrestingly queer to the eye that discovers it. Even when alive it seems to be dead for its horny legs move only a fraction of a millimetre at a time and with the slowest motion imaginable.

The only sea-spider apt to be noticed at all on the tideline is the comparatively short-legged kind here. This is **Pycnogonum littorale**, which clings to sea anemones, stabs them with its long beak and sucks their juices, but does not usually "bleed" them to death. The host may succumb when too many parasites fasten upon it, but that does not happen very often. We have other kinds of sea-spider, but they are almost phantom creatures, with legs so long and thin that they remain invisible unless sought for with great deliberation and patience in rock pools or among a collection of sea creatures gathered into an aquarium. I have discerned some of these clinging to the rosy polyp crowns of oaten-pipe hydroids on Gorleston breakwater at low spring tides and specimens are sometimes brought up among the rubbish in shrimp trawls.

In less turbid seas, where anemones and corallines dwell in the limpid depths, many sea-spiders are to be found. Some of them are constructed like birds' nests, others have dozens of leg-like outgrowths in addition to their eight true legs.

They are masters of the art of camouflage in shape, colour and behaviour, and they move with the utmost stealth. Some are as translucent as the shadowy waters, others are crimson on crimson hosts, yellow on yellow, green on green, and so on. In the greater depths they share the blindness of the majority of sea-creatures that dwell in perpetual gloom. And there, where colour serves no optical purpose, they are all red, like the deep-sea prawns.

The Sea Spider -
*Pychogonum
littorale*

Said to Stop Sea Sickness

Blakeney, Wells and Scolt Head 29/2/63

If you explore the tidal creeks at Blakeney, Wells and Scolt Head, you will sometimes come across the remarkable molluscs known as coat-of-mail shells, usually attached to weedy flint stones.

These are slug-shaped creatures whose shells consist of eight transverse plates, interlocked in such a way as to allow the animal to curl up like a wood-louse. The ones found on this coast may grow to almost an inch in length and they are mostly a greenish colour, matching the weed-stained surface of the stones.

I have seen only one species here: **Lepidochitona cinereus**, but many others, some of which are beautifully variegated and tufted with spines, or covered with velvet down, creep over the sea-bathed rocks along more rugged coasts

Like limpets, these molluscs browse on films of the more microscopic kinds of seaweeds encrusting the rocks and, again like limpets, they have definite resting-places to which they return after each expedition in search of food.

Curiously enough, they are totally blind. They move very slowly, feeling their way along and scraping off the weeds with row upon row of sharp, horny teeth as they go.

Although they have no eyes, it appears that they are in some way sensitive to light, because they are most active at night and hardly ever take up resting positions in which they will be exposed to light during the day. This keeps them out of sight of shore-haunting birds, except turnstones and perhaps purple sandpipers which investigate every chink and look for food under overhanging rocks when the tide is out.

The eggs, which have a tough skin, are laid in clusters on the rocks. The young are equipped with knobbly eyes and swimming organs, both of which they lose when they have grown their shell plates and settle down to a creeping life.

Icelandic fishermen are said to swallow these armadillo-like creatures, which they call "sea-bugs", to prevent sea sickness. I have never heard of them being used by our own fishermen for this purpose; but since their bodies are peculiarly glutinous, they might well prove efficacious in holding down one's breakfast on a rough voyage.

British coat-of-mail shells are all quite small, but in tropical seas some species grow as much as eight inches long. In the West Indies, the shell plates of large specimens are cut off and the fleshy parts are chewed and swallowed raw. They are said to taste as good as oysters. Despite their origin in the sea, they are considered thirst-quenching, whereas oysters promote a thirst for ale.

"Sand Castles" Built by Worms

East Anglian Coast 17/12/59

Scouring tides sometimes dislodge quantities of certain seaweeds and creatures that dwell close inshore on the sea bed, just below the region exposed at the lowest ebbs. "Lows" between sand ridges off our East Anglian coast and, in some parts, hollows in the flint-strewn chalk where currents sweep in close, often teem with anchored colonies of feathery hydroids, sponges, dahlia anemonies and finger-shaped growths of polyps, clustered among long ribbons of brown oar-weeds and delicate, plume-like red seaweeds.

Long-armed, fragile starfish jostle in thousands in hollows fringed with star-spangled sea squirts. Hermit crabs, in borrowed whelk shells, march, robber like, over beds of corallines, while little squids, spangled with brilliant colours, speed, goggle-eyed, between the outward streaming weeds overhead. Under the stress of storms, these niches so rich in life may be swept clear or else buried under sand and sludge. On our unstable coast, so much at the mercy of the elements, no lodging is secure in less than five fathoms of water.

One of the more fragile victims of the scours is the golden-comb worm, **Pectinaria koreni**. Broken pieces of its sandy, horn-shaped tubes are washed up commonly enough; but once in a while, quantities of the tubes, with their occupants still within, drift ashore. The worms construct their homes of carefully-selected grains of sand, which are cemented with a natural marine glue.

They have delicate tentacles, like pale pink threads, which are used in finding food and collecting sand grains. Beyond the tentacles extend two combs of shining golden bristles, used for scooping out hollows in the sand, for filtering off the coarser materials while-feeding is in progress and for drawing in tightly over the aperture of the tube, like a lid, by way of protection.

Some years ago, I managed to keep one of these comb-worms alive in a jar of sea water for a few days. Until then, I had imagined that its habit would be to nestle in the sand with its head protruding; but instead, it buried its head in the sand at the bottom of the jar and almost vanished, leaving only the extreme tip of the tail end of its tube projecting (even this was hard to distinguish, because the sand was of the same tint). From time to time a thin stream of fine sand particles was ejected from the tail while burrowing was going on.

Another worm building tubes of sand off our coast is not so much at the mercy of storms, because it lives in colonies, with the tubes forming a honey comb-like masses, cementing almost as firmly as sandstone rock. This is **Sabellaria alveolata**, a reef-builder which sometimes gives threshold protection to our piers, as at Gorleston in the 1920s when great masses of it helped to ward off the fury of waves in the South Ham as they swept into the concrete breakwater.

Water Witches of Suffolk

Suffolk 1/7/61

Mariners have many strange tales to tell of unexplained apparitions met with by night and by day on ocean voyages; but apart from the Loch Ness monster, creatures are seldom reported from mainland waters, in our own country, at least.

One wild inhabitant of Suffolk estuaries may be mentioned as an exception to this rule. On the rare occasions it has been encountered, the observers have always experienced a peculiar feeling of incredulity. I refer to the remarkable mollusc, **Akera bullata,** which has been called a water witch.

From time to time these witches have been performing strange antics on brackish ditches and on calm waters covering mudflats at high tide, in April and May. They flit and flap over the surface in a lively fashion, threshing the water with broad, fleshy fins, which they wrap about their bodies like a cloak when they rest for a moment. Their heads are thrust forward like snouted prehistoric monsters; their middle parts are encased in shining, bubble-like shells, while from the rear trail long white single threads.

When extended during these exercises they are about three inches long, and nearly as broad across the spotted "wings." Even when one knows what they are, there is something uncanny about their motions; such hilarity and dancing is not expected in snails and slugs, to which order these creatures belong. If they were larger, they would be terrifying and as it is, I have known naturalists who confessed to having been mesmerised when confronted by what Lewis Carroll must have meant by his "slithy toves".

Their ecstasies, like many other animal displays, are connected with the nuptial season. If one drags forth waterweeds from the salt ditches where the witches are at play, they will be found knotted with golden ropes, twisted both ways. These are Akera's egg capsules.

Perhaps the Norfolk coast is not quite warm enough for the witches; I have never heard of them being seen farther north than the Suffolk Alde on this side of England.

They are not the only lively molluscs, if one goes farther afield. Warm seas are thronged by rather similar creatures callled sea-butterflies, which raise their wings like miniature sails and glide along. Then there is the wonderful nautilus, whose pale, delicate shell behaves as a sail. Octopuses, cuttlefish, and giant squids, all masters of underwater speed, the last being among the real monsters of the deep, are but highly developed molluscs.

Heavenly Blue Drifts

Norfolk and Suffolk Coast 27/7/57

In July, the salt marshes of the Wash coast, round to Cley, and those of the Suffolk estuaries, are bright with the flowers of sea lavender, crisply spriggy and papery almost to the point of artificiality on a close view, but when seen in great drifts stretching down to the water, more heavenly than the blue sky itself. The mud and the sea wrack are obscured in the twinkle of a million amethysts. The moment of perfection is soon gone, but vivid colour lurks in the backward patches for several weeks.

I associate the common sea lavender with another flaring-up of colour on the salt flats. Many people must have noticed it without connecting it specially with this plant. I refer to the rich scarlet and orange which colours tens of thousands of the sea lavender leaves just before the flowers open. The leaves so gorgeously inflamed owe their transfiguration to the activities of their own special rust fungus; it stains them scarlet and itself emerges in the form of orange cluster-cups, richly embossing the surfaces.

Later in the summer, the cluster-cups vanish and the fungus produces bluish lead-coloured glistening blisters on the leaves and stems. The rust attacks only the common sea lavender (**Limonium vulgare**) and is present wherever the plant grows on our coast. Honey bees obtain a great deal of nectar from these flowers, which are visited also by innumerable bumble-bees. It is amusing to see the latter flying from their nests in the sandhills and crossing the water filling the creeks at high tide, to visit the sea lavender blossoms almost submerged on the flooded saltings. The plants are visited also by many other kinds of insects, including the males of a rare salt marsh horse fly.

One would think that the risk of frequent submergence in salt water would discourage insects from attempting to live on sea lavender regularly, but a small violet-coloured metallic weevil does so, and so does a curious little plume moth which is in the habit of folding its pale brown wings so as to appear like a fragment of dead stick.

Three other kinds of sea lavender are to be found on the Norfolk coast. The largest of these might be mistaken for a rank and lax-flowered variety of the common species. This is **Limonium humile**, which is rather rare and grows in muddy places, usually where the sea aster flourishes best. The matted sea lavender (**Statice bellidifolium**) has small pinkish flowers produced in wiry rosettes on the drier sandy margins of our saltings and in this country it is confined to the coast of East Anglia. Our fourth species is one of the rock lavenders, **L. binervosum**; it grows in stiff tufts on shingle ridges adjoining the salt marshes, but not on the beaches where the shingle is loose. It is distinguished easily by its three-veined leaf stalks.

Waxing fat on Sea Wormwood

East Anglian Coast 20/1/73

Sea Wormwood (***Artemisia maritima***) is a common plant on the higher and drier fringes of the salt marshes and flood-banks in all the estuarine regions of East Anglia and on warm summer days it gives a very pleasant spicy "tang" to the sea air.

Its sprigs of finely divided leaves are silvery with hairs which help to conserve moisture and the slender, shrubby stems spring from very tough deeply-established woody rootstocks year after year. Small golden or reddish flower-clusters mature in August and September, in nodding spikes a foot to eighteen inches high.

Like the cultivated wormwood, this strongly aromatic and bitter herb has in the past been put to many uses. Boiled with rice or made into a confection with honey, it was regarded as the most effective medicine for expelling worms.

It was sometimes gathered by "good religious fathers" for the preparation of absinthe, but one must assume that it contributed nothing but flavour, fragrance and medicinal virtue to their concoctions, since it was, in itself, credited with the ability to prevent people from getting drunk if they took a dose of it first thing in the morning.

There is an ancient reference to its effect on grazing animals: "such beeves, sheep and cattell as feede upon Sea Wormwood, do waxe very fat" and I am inclined to think that the animals in these circumstances thrived because they were regularly de-wormed as a result of taking nature's own cure.

Wormwoods and mugwort (a less bitter plant of the same genus) have been much used in brewing beers at various periods and even within living memory bunches of them, dried, have been kept in ale-houses for putting into mulled beer.

The taste for these things seems to have been lost; but there has been a great revival of home brewing recently, so there may be some who will go so far as to experiment with herbal additives which were savoured with delight by our hard working, hard drinking forbears.

My old mentor A H Patterson (John Knowlittle) used to keep a sprig of the sea wormwood in his study and sniff it once in a while to remind him of Breydon or a tramp along the North Norfolk coast. There could be no more exciting pot-pourri.

Mugwort - "Poor Man's Tobacco"

Norfolk 8/2/69

Mugwort (**Artemisia vulgaris**), a tall, shaggy, grey-green weed of waste ground, seems to flourish greatly on derelict building sites in towns and even to dominate them quite often.

It is seen less frequently now in cornfields or even round the headlands, since farms have become more efficiently mechanised and herbicides are used more extensively.

In open countryside, however, the verges often produce conspicuous crops of this plant for a few years following road-widening, while other patches can be seen bordering railway tracks.

I can remember the days when one would find a bunch of dried mugwort hung up in a village pub during the winter months, the sprigs being used to give a special "tang" and savour to mulled ale which some of the old countrymen preferred to the cold stuff drawn from the wood on a winter's night.

The name "mugwort" originated from this association. In East Anglia this plant is very commonly known as "Poor Man's Tobacco" on account of its frequent use, when dried, as a major constituent of herbal tobacco, along with the white-felt leaves of coltsfoot. The smoke has a pleasant, sweetish aroma but at times is almost as pungent as that of wormwood; the quality of the scent varies considerably in mugwort plants and I have found that the most pungent specimens usually come from dry, sunny sites.

Bunches of this plant are sometimes placed in linen chests, like lavender, to discourage clothes moths but wormwood is more valuable as a moth deterrent.

In the Middle Ages the placing of a sprig of mugwort, or its near relative the sea wormwood (plentiful on the North Norfolk coast) under the pillow at night was said to provoke delight and exotic dreams, but I have not tried its efficiency in this respect.

The jagged, chrysanthemum-like leaves are silvery beneath, and the small flower-heads may be almost white, or tipped with red, or honey-coloured.

In ancient times quantities of the flowers used to be placed in hogsheads of beer to preserve them from "fowzing" or "going foisty" as we would say in Norfolk.

Mugwort - *Artemisia vulgaris*

Fortunes of the Sand Wasp

Norfolk 3/8/57

While picnicking in an old sandpit or in a hollow behind the coast dunes on a hot summer's day, one is very likely, sooner or later, to catch sight of a sand wasp and to become interested in its activities. There are several kinds of these slender-bodied wasps, which make solitary burrows in which they place living anaesthetised prey in store as food for their grubs. Some of them may be seen dragging spiders, craneflies or weevils over the sand and, quite frequently, the victim is larger than its captor.

The most conspicuous is the red-banded ***Ammophila sabulosa***. It is slightly under an inch long and has a black and orange-red banded body and smoky-tipped wings.

I once spent several hours following the fortunes of a female Ammophila. First, she chose a little patch of bare sandy soil and began to excavate a vertical burrow by removing the harder lumps with her jaws and scratching out the looser material with her legs, rather like a scratching hen.

She worked furiously and seemed to be set on taking advantage of the slight dampness retained by the sand overnight, which reduced the risk of the sides of the burrow caving in while the excavation was in progress. It took about three hours for the tunnel to be dug to a depth of about two and a half inches and the work was completed just before midday. Then the wasp very quickly found a piece of gravel just large enough to plug the entrance, and after fussing round and whisking a few more grains of soil over the top, she flew off. I followed her flight and presently discovered her in the act of stinging a fairly large bright green caterpillar at the roots of a tuft of grass about 30 feet from the burrow.

The caterpillar was not struggling, and I gained the impression that the wasp had given it a preliminary injection earlier to paralyse it. The wasp then dragged the caterpillar over the ground all the way to its burrow. I expected the insect to make an air reconnaissance from time to time, but it never did so. The journey took an erratic course through the undergrowth and under a wire fence and was accomplished in just over an hour. The wasp either possessed an unerring homing instinct or else knew every bit of the territory as a result of earlier intensive hunting. On arrival at the hole, the prey was dropped for a few moments while the plug was removed from the entrance. Ammophila plunged into the burrow and inspected it briefly, after which she dragged the caterpillar inside, paused to lay an egg on its body and emerged into the sunshine. She lost no time in filling up the hole with loose, sandy earth, which was partly scraped in by the feet and partly inserted with the mandibles. A largish piece of gravel was again used as a final stopper and this in turn was concealed by fine dust scratched over it. The wasp then preened herself and flew off, either to plan another such operation or to enjoy much-needed refreshment from flowers.

Puffball Stalk is Sand Anchor

Norfolk 23/11/63

Ripe puffballs of various kinds are specially noticeable in autumn. They include monsters up to eighteen inches high which look like giant white egg-heads of Humpty-Dumpties peeping from hedges and nettle beds in September, purple-brown "hedgehog" puffers in the woods, small flattish, mealy ones on the lawns and others studded with pyramidal warts and star-pointed meshes, clustered on rotten tree trunks.

At first they are soft and pale yellow or olive tinted inside, but later they become packed with brown or curry-coloured fluff and millions of dry, powdery spores, while the outer covering of skin turns from parchment into thin but tough and waterproof paper. In some of the larger kinds, the skin breaks away in pieces, allowing the wind to tear at the fluff and whisk away the spores. More often the puffballs have a single nipple-like pore and if they are poked or squeezed, the spores emerge like smoke from a funnel. Raindrops hitting ripe puffballs cause them to puff gently and produce little smoke rings (this has been demonstrated by flash-photography); the heavy drops falling from trees are more effective than ordinary raindrops, while lumps of hail are better still. After a squeezing, the skin becomes taut again.The spores are extremely small and ornamented with tiny warts which help to keep them airborne and later give them a grip when they reach the ground.

One kind of puffball which we find occasionally in Norfolk grows on long, thin stalks out of sand. It is never more than two inches high, with a "puffer" at themost half an inch in diameter. This is ***Tulostoma brumale***, which flourishes on calcareous dunes and the tops of old walls which provide a substrata of weathered mortar. In both situations the fungus is often associated with mosses of the genus Tortula.

The Rev Charles Sutton, Rector of Holme and Vicar of Thornham in 1794, appears to have been the first Norfolk botanist to collect the little Tulostoma, which he sent for illustration in Sowerby's "English Fungi". It can still be found on the dunes at Holme, Holkham, Scolt Head and Blakeney Point, but seldom in any quantity. In the 19th century it was known to flourish on certain ancient walls in St Faith's Lane in Norwich and at New Catton, and a Norfolk mycologist came upon it growing between granite sets in King Street, King's Lynn, in 1898, and on a garden wall at Heacham.

It seems that ***Tulostoma's*** long stalk is necessary for two reasons; the mycelium must be well buried in order to obtain moisture in the sand, while the "puffer" must be exposed on the surface. Even when some of the sand becomes very dry and blows away, the fungus remains anchored by its stalk.

26

Living Jewels of Cliff and Dune

Norfolk 3/8/63

Burnet moths are sometimes plentiful along our cliffs and dunes at the beginning of August. They are like living jewels. Their plump, heavy bodies are clothed in black velvet, their hind wings are crimson and their forewings iridescent green or black with crimson spots. They fly deliberately, like bumble bees and seldom travel far at a time. It is most usual to find them clinging to grass stalks alongside the tough yellow silken cocoons from which they have recently emerged.

The caterpillars are rather rotund, softly hairy creatures of sluggish form and disposition, pale yellow, with rows of dark dots and crescents. They feed, mainly at night, on various clovers and trefoils, but invariably climb the stems of tall grasses and rushes when the time comes for them to spin cocoons. These cocoons are very conspicuous, but it seems that they are seldom attacked successfully by birds, the reason being that they are too tough to tackle on the grass stalks, since these do not give the birds enough support when it comes to holding on and pecking.

They are not without enemies, however. Sometimes tiny black braconid wasps parasitise them heavily and when the caterpillars are preparing to pupate on the grass stalks, dozens of little grubs come out of their bodies and spin clusters of their own silken cocoons alongside the shrivelled remains of their victims.

Burnet moths fly in bright sunshine, visiting flowers with bees and butterflies in the heat of the day. Those seen on the coast are usually of the kind that have six red spots on each of its forewings, but on rush-meadows on many of our inland commons and round the Broads, the commoner species is the five spot burnet, which sometimes visits the flowers of orchids and is very successful in fertilising them.

Here and there in fenny spots where its food plant, common sorrel, is plentiful, a metallic green burnet moth called the "forester" may be seen buzzing about. It looks quite exotic, especially when it is visiting the pink flowers of ragged robin along with various summer butterfies.

Altogether there are 10 species of burnets and foresters in the British Isles, but as far as I am aware only the three I mentioned occur in Norfolk. One is peculiar to the New Forest, others to the mountains and chalk downs. They have many things in common, including the habit of gregariousness. If you find one burnet moth you may be reasonably certain the there is a well established colony near by. Because these insects do not fly far, close inbreeding often takes place, with the result that well-marked local varieties have been evolved in many different places. One striking form of the six spot burnet has yellow instead of crimson wing-colouration.

Bird-Like Moths

8/10/83

Humming-bird hawk moths have proved a source of mystery for many people in various parts of Norfolk this year (1983). They have been mistaken for miniature humming birds on several occasions, as my correspondence reveals.

They certainly give this impression as they hover over flowers with wings whirring so fast as to seem almost invisible, while the long proboscis (a tubular tongue) is thrust briefly into each blossom, like a slender beak.

The similarity goes even further, in that black, white and grey feather-like tufts spread like a tail from the hind part of the mouse-grey body, contrasting with the tawny hue of the wings. Even the beady eyes glisten like those of a bird. These fast-flying moths are able to breed all the year round in North Africa and at the end of winter they send forth swarms of migrants heading northward from the Mediterranean across Europe. Some reach Britain every year so far as southern counties are concerned, but their spread into East Anglia tends to occur late in the season after the immigrants have produced broods in the south. This year, a few reached us in June and from early August onwards the local stock increased noticably to reach a peak by mid-September, when these visitants came to garden flowers such as phlox and red valerian in many places.

The caterpillars feed chiefly on yellow lady's bedstraw, a hay-scented, sprawling plant which carpets sandy ground especially in coastal areas, but also on many of our drier commons inland. Massive immigrations of humming-bird moths take place at irregular intervals and not very often so far as this county is concerned. In the last hundred years those of 1899, 1937, 1943 and 1947 were most noteworthy, that of 1947 proving an all-time record, when a glorious summer favoured the insects both here and elsewhere in Europe.

Normally the insects do not survive here in winter and many of those emerging towards the end of the season undertake a return migration southward and may be seen travelling in great numbers through the valleys in the Pyrenees. Following the 1947 irruption, however, a few actually passed the winter successfully, to reappear in March, but the summer of that year proved fickle and their achievement came to nought.

Common Plant of Verges

19/4/58

Many miles of hedge banks along most of our roads within a few miles of the coast are clothed with the vivid yellow-green foliage of a coarse, celery-like plant at this time of the year (April); but although it is so common few people I have met have been able to put a name to it, except in suggesting that it might be some sort of horse parsley, or cow parsnip, or even hemlock and probably poisonous.

Its official English name today is "Alexanders"; three hundred years ago it was "Alexander" or "Alisandere", the black pot-herb or "Olus atrum" of the ancients, Our name seems to have originated as a corruption of the Latin epithet, which has been perpetuated in Linnaeus's name for the plant, *Smyrnium olusatrum*. We must get rid of any idea that the herb was ever associated historically with any of the famous figures bearing the name of Alexander. In North Norfolk they call it "Horse Peppers". Botanists are by no means certain that this is a true native of the British Isles, although it is freely distributed round our coasts and occurs in a fair number of inland localities nowadays. This difficulty arises from the fact that the plant was in regular cultivation by monks and others in medieval times. The crowns were earthed up and blanched, for eating raw, like celery, before the latter had been introduced to popular taste.

The green tops also used to be boiled as a vegetable, while the large black seeds (sold as Macedonian parsley) were used for flavouring savoury dishes and taken medicinally for a variety of ills, including snake bite. Alexanders is a common wayside species of the Mediterranean countries, but not of the mainland in western Europe and this fact again points to the plant having been introduced here by human agency, so it is probably best to regard it as a long-naturalised alien.

In East Anglia it has a curious distribution. It abounds within about three miles of the sea all along the coast and grows also on the flanks of all our river valleys, penetrating right to their sources. Over the rest of the countryside it is absent from the hedge banks, but is to be seen occasionally about old ruins. So far, no one has been able to explain why it follows the rivers inland or, for that matter, why it grows so successfully near the sea; but perhaps sea-mists and marsh mists will be found to provide an answer in the long run. Alexanders, like many other umbelliferous plants such as carrot and parsnip, is a biennial. The seedlings come up very early in the spring and the young plants are evergreen through the winter and die after seeding in the following year. The yellow-green flowers flourish from March to June and are visited mainly by flies and beetles, but occasionally also by honey bees.

Natterjacks

10/7/54

It is unfortunate that the natterjack, most pretty of the toads, has now all but vanished from the East Anglian scene.

There were fenny haunts within afew miles of the coast where, up to 20 years ago, one could meet with lively swarms of these "running toads", as they were known. They repaired to sandy field banks for hibernation, usually snuggling together in large numbers, large and small, cheek by jowl, in disused rabbit burrows and the like. In May (seldom earlier) they would run out like mice and the adults would make tracks for the nearest shallow water to undertake the business of spawning, the smaller specimens retiring into holes close to their winter haunts by day. In the breeding season one could hear the ventriloquial trilling of natterjacks all about the marshes, especially on mild nights at glow-worm time. At Reedham, these toads were known as "May-birds" for that reason.

I used to know them at Gorleston, Belton, Fritton and Southwold; but they appear to have become very scarce in all these localities. There are still a few within a mile or two of Reedham, but it is clear that their survival anywhere in this part of the country is threatened by rural developments of several kinds, while road casualties at certain times of the year can reduce a local colony considerably.

These toads have an age-old connection with the sea coast and estuaries and they are well used to spawning in shallow, brackish water. If they were less particular in their choice of homes they might be more widespread and enjoy at least as great a chance of survival here as common toads. The matter may be connected with climate, of course, for it is well known that even in this part of England, the sea tempers the frost and summer heat equally in our coastal belt.

The natterjack has a bright and clean appearance at all times. His eyes sparkle like emeralds; his back is richly patterned with mottlings of various greens and strawberry pink, neatly divided by a primrose yellow strip running down the backbone line. Underneath, he is creamy white like a kid glove. He runs in quick sallies which come to a stop suddenly. In the dusk, a natterjack's spurt, followed by the cessation of all movement, makes one wonder whether the movement was only imagined. Sitting still the mottling and yellow strip merge with the sand dune vegetation, moss, lichen and sea spurge.

Running toads will sometimes come out to pick up insects and worms after a summer shower, in daylight. When a moving object is observed, the toad makes a rush to within a few inches of its intended prey, pauses, twitching the middle toes of its hind feet in excitement for a moment before its tongue lashes out and in with a greedy click. The prey is swallowed with a certain pleasurable ritual of eye closing, neck stretching and drawing in of the sides. If the object is a worm, it is wiped clean with the hands in a most comical fashion. I once saw a natterjack sweep baby frogs into its mouth one after another; but it spat them out unharmed.

Barnacles Cut Speedboat Power

Hardley, River Chet 4/8/73

A speedboat put in the water in May at Hardley, where the river Chet joins the Yare, found that by mid July the underside was so thickly encrusted with barnacles, which even coated the propeller, that planing proved impossible through loss of power.

The owner was astonished that this trouble should have arisen in more or less fresh water. However, the barnacles in this instance were of a brackish-water species *(Balanus improvisus)* occurring commonly in Yarmouth haven and in the vicinity of Breydon.

When trading wherries made frequent calls at Yarmouth and lay there off and on, their bottoms often became colonised by these crustaceans. In the long summer drought of 1921, when tidal salts moved farther up our local rivers than usual, the barnacles became established temporarily up to Acle on the Bure and in the lower reaches of the Waveney and Oulton Dyke.

After the sea flooded Horsey Mere and other broads in that region in February, 1938, barnacles became abundant, covering not only submerged wood and stones, but also reed stems. Curiously enough, I do not remember a similar swarming after the sea flooding of 1953, which was much more extensive.

Successful colonisation depends on conditions being right for settlement when the minute swimming larvae *(nauplii)* of the barnacles are present, normally from May to September.

Once the infant barnacles become fixed, they grow very rapidly and reach full size by the end of July, thereafter dying off at the end of summer after a period of active reproduction. Grown specimens attain a diameter of about half an inch and have six white wall-plates forming a cone. They secrete a limy base which often remains when the shells have disappeared.

This species inhabits estuaries on bothsides of the Atlantic and is widespread in the Baltic where it tolerates virtually a freshwater environment in reed-beds along the coast of Finland. Darwin named it improvisus, aptly indicating its adaptable nature. In one respect, however, it is not tolerant; unlike some barnacles, it cannot stand frequent exposure to the air between tidemarks.

Prawns Living in Freshwater

The Broads 30/1/60

Visitors to the Broads are sometimes rather astonished to find prawns up to three inches long living in freshwater.

These adventurous crustaceans are often abundant in Oulton Broad, which is usually a little brackish, and they are very plentiful in Breydon Water, which is estuarine. One finds them as far up the river Bure as Wroxham occasionally and they have been taken from Barton Broad and in the waters connecting the Thurne river, where at least a trace of salt is always present.

For generations, Breydon fishermen have known them as "Jack Shrimps" or "Breydon Shrimps", distinguished by their white colour, but it was not until 1921 that the late Dr Robert Gurney discovered that they were of a species not previously recognised in Britain. He found that they were *Palaemon longirostris*, a river and estuary prawn well known in Holland, in the Mediterranean region and in some estuaries of western France. He found that they could be kept easily in freshwater aquaria, if fed on pieces of worm or raw meat, and experiments show that they were so indifferent to changes in salinity that they could be transferred from fresh to salt water and vice versa without injury.

Another prawn of about the same size (*Leander squilla*), common inshore along the Norfolk coast, also enters estuaries occasionally. In life it has purple stripes on its body, yellow bands on the legs and touches of blue on some of its claws, whereas P. longirostris is practically colourless, although it may have a trace of greyish or purplish banding occasionally, and it becomes an opaque white immediately at death.

Our river prawn is migratory. During the greater part of the year it ranges from brackish to quite fresh water, but in summer, for the purpose of breeding, it goes down to the saltier parts of estuaries and the sea. Spawning takes place only when the eggs are on the verge of hatching. The larvae are carried out to sea by the tides and do not return to the rivers until they are nearly ready to cast off their infant coats and assume the adult form. They return as little prawns about six millimetres long. I have seen them as small as half an inch from snout to tail in Horsey Mere.

Large specimens are often taken in eel-setts and eel-pots in the Broadland rivers and they still swarm in Breydon, despite Yarmouth's pollution. Curiously enough, there appears to be no record of their having been marketed as edible by the old Breydoners. It may be that their dead white appearance was prejudicial.

There is still a mystery about the local distribution of the river prawn. It is not known to inhabit any part of East Anglia other than the river system of the Broads. Elsewhere in Britain specimens have been found in the Tamar, near Plymouth.

Adventures of Baby Flounders

Norfolk 19/2/55

Freshwater anglers never cease to express astonishment at capturing a flatfish far inland and when they do take such a fish, these are usually thought to be either plaice or dabs, whereas they invariably turn out to be flounders. As a matter of fact, small flounders, about the size of a penny, travel up all our Norfolk rivers as far as the first locks quite regularly and they enter all small tributary streams encountered on the way. Not only are they quite at home in fresh water, but they make a habit of going after the rich variety of food in the shape of aquatic insects, crustacea and molluscs present in our rivers.

From time to time, they even enter the Broads and wax fat there in company with roach and bream. They are not often taken with rod and line, but this is to be accounted for by the fact that most of them are rather small and because the tend to lie in the mud with only their eyes and mouths protruding.

At the onset of cold weather in late autumn, most of the up-river flounders scuttle downstream to the estuaries, or at all events to the region of brackish waters. All through the winter, larger specimens abound in estuary and coastal waters and it used to be the custom of Yarmouth fishermen to go butt-darting on Breydon at that season. Flounders have always been called "butts"in that district, and the "darts" used for their capture were barbed forks on shafts about 20 feet long, handled rather in the manner of eel-picks from boats.

Flounders in breeding condition make their exodus from the estuaries towards the end of February and migrate to certain deeps in the North Sea, where spawning takes place in early spring. Their rate of travelling has been estimated as about four miles a day, but must vary greatly according to the tidal currents met with at some stages of the journey.

Although the eggs are laid in deep water, they rise to the surface and are there fertilised. The young find their way in time to coastal waters and in their turn enter the mouths of rivers to seek freshwater adventures. These fish are able to withstand pollution extremely well, and in the vicinity of Yarmouth they may be found stained deeply with various chemical effluents and yet seem to be in quite good condition.

The flesh of flounders, especially in fresh water, tends to be watery and inferior to that of the sand dabs and plaice caught in the sea. At one time they were considered fit for little except baiting lobster pots in this part of the country. They were also put to a rather curious use at Yarmouth, being plastered on the chests of children suffering from whooping-cough.

Eating Soup with Chopsticks

Norfolk Broads 25/7/81

Almost any sample of water taken from a weedy pond or ditch will be found to contain a large number of minute crustaceans. Many of them will prove to be copepods, few of which reach a length of more than one millimetre.

In spite of their small size, they can be recognised by their jerky, erratic movements achieved partly by the vigorous rowing action of their two long antennae and partly by less conspicuous bristly limbs.

Under magnification they can be seen to possess a single eye, commonly red or black, in the centre of the "forehead". It is from this that the genus *Cyclops*, to which most of our freshwater copepods belong, has derived its name.

Legions of these little animals also flourish in the seas, from pole to pole, forming a major part of the plankton which feeds fishes and other creatures, including whales which filter them off in bulk through curtains of whalebone fibres. In some regions, at certain times of the year, the sea may be pink with them and some marine scientists have gone so far as to contemplate the possibility of catching and processing them in bulk as human food.

The Norfolk Broads used to be very rich in these creatures, along with cladocerans or "water fleas". The late Dr Robert Gurney had identified more than 40 species in samples taken from these waters at the beginning of this century and he later went on to write our standard monograph on freshwater copepods, many of which he found able to withstand brackish conditions in our local waterways. Cyclops (see illustration) scrabbles food particles into its mouth with minute "chopstick" limbs. Green algae coating the side of an aquarium are devoured in this way, as are diatoms attached to aquatic plants or lying on mud. One can sometimes see a "soup" of this green food lying darkly within the translucent body of the copepod.

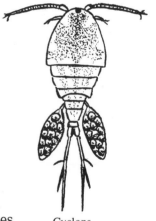

Cyclops

The females trail a pair of egg bags containing relatively large eggs and these are often red, though occasionally of some other striking colour: even bright blue. The larvae emerging from these eggs are equipped with well-developed bristly legs and relatively short antennae until the time comes for them to discard their infant coats and assume adult form.

One finds a succession of these creatures reaching abundance at different seasons. Only shallow water species occur in Norfolk, but in some of Britain's lakes the extreme depths are inhabited by peculiar forms, as are the depths of the oceans.

Fairy Shrimp of Mousehold

Mousehold Heath 1/3/75

In many parts of the world and especially on the fringes of deserts where rain falls only at rare intervals, various of the smaller types of aquatic creatures manage to survive by means of eggs capable of remaining caked in dry mud if needs be for several years, waiting for water to return.

There are many small crustaceans equipped for this kind of existence, including water-fleas and copepods which, because they are so adaptable in this way, make use even of very temporary shallow puddles at various seasons.

They gain one advantage from adopting this way of life, in that they avoid having to compete with a vast assortmenof other creatures inhabiting permanent waters. They are a select few, along with certain algae which have adopted the same habit and supply the plant life of the short-lived pools. The largest crustacean to appear in shallow ephemeral sheets of water in this country is the fairy shrimp (***Chirocephalus diaphanus***), but it turns up only rarely.

Having made its appearance in great numbers in a little pond on Mousehold Heath, near Norwich, in 1762, it has never reappeared in Norfolk. However, I was fortunate enough to see it flourishing in a field hollow in Cambridgeshire earlier this month (written 1/3/75). It was obvious that the site had been quite dry last summer, having been ploughed and cropped with maize. Autumn rains had cupped in the clayey hollow, however, to form a shallow pool in which the fairy shrimps, hatching from eggs in the soil, had been able to grow to maturity in the winter months.

Many of them were over an inch long, and they were swimming on their backs with the help of feathered legs which in this animal serve both as lungs and food-gatherers. They had stalked black eyes and red tips to their tails and legs. Otherwise they appeared almost transparent, except for the greenish egg-bags trailed by the mature female.

I have searched a few likely-looking field ponds in the hope of finding them elsewhere recently, but so far without success. However conditions are very promising just now, following last year's dry summer, so perhaps someone may be fortunate enough to rediscover these fascinating, very primitive crustaceans in this county after a lapse of more than two hundred years.

Indian Rope Trick

Norfolk 5/5/79

Among our freshwater molluscs, the bladder snails are peculiar in having a left-handed (sinistral) twist to their shells.

One species (***Physa fontinalis***) is very common in healthy ponds, dykes and streams, where it may be found creeping in a lively fashion over the leaves of aquatic plants at almost all seasons. Although living almost submerged for most of the time, I have noticed that it also has a habit of leaving the water for short periods, like the wandering mud snail, especially at night. Its hardiness is not in doubt, for I am meeting with swarms of this species in shallow fen pools which were frozen solid at times during the past winter.

The snail is about the size of an orange pip, the shell being very glossy, thin and horn coloured, but so translucent that the black body within makes it appear dark in life. The body more than fills the shell and overlaps it in a lobed fringe. In crawling the wedge-shaped "tail" and the head, with its thin, pale tentacles, are conspicuous.

The feeding antics of bladder snails suggest that they are more interested in scraping off and engulfing microscopic algae than in devouring the leaves of pondweeds. Sometimes they glide upside down at the surface of the water, imbibing what they need from the floating film.

When making progress over mud in the depths, they secrete a copious flow of slime which congeals to form extensive rope-like tracks giving them support. On occasions, the slime-threads are gathered into loops, like the lifelines of some spiders. Perhaps the most remarkable use to which these threads are put is in acting as ladders between the bottom of the pond and the surface, whereby the snails appear to perform an "Indian rope trick".

We have also the Moss Bladder Snail (***Aplexa hypnorum***) in Norfolk: but this is rare and only met with occasionally. Its more slender, elongated and pointed shape makes it easy to distinguish, while the body is relatively less bulky and does not curl into lobes wrapping the base of the shell. It occurs mainly in shallow, mossy pools which dry out in summer and is often associated with the Flote-grass (***Glyceria fluitans***) whose slender, floating leaves extend over the water surface. There are several records of this species from the Fenland region, but only a very few from East Norfolk (Colney and Thorpe). A careful search of the many shallow pools which are a feature of various village greens and commons might well reveal its presence in many more places. Several other kinds of bladder snails flourish in some of Britain's canals, lakes and garden pools following their introduction from abroad, but so far these have not turned up in this county.

Parasite's odd behaviour

Wheatfen 27/8/55

I have witnessed strange performances on the part of amber snails in reed swamps on Surlingham marshes. In each case the snail has been perched high on a marsh plant, while a grub like creature within its body has thrust itself outward into one of the snail's eye-tentacles as into the finger of a glove and worked backwards and forwards in a rhythmic action. The tentacle becomes greatly stretched in the process, but regains its normal form when the queer occupant retires intot the body cavity of its host at the end of the display.

The parasite is cylindrical and maggot-like in form. Its head end is decorated with black spots and the rest of the body is banded alternately with dark green and white bands, which make it conspicuous. When at rest its colours can be seen inside the translucent yellowish body of the snail.

The creature is a trematode worm, which in its adult form is a fluke, like the well-known liver fluke of sheep, in this case living in the bodies of marsh birds such as moorhens and water rail. The fluke's eggs pass out with the parasitised bird's droppings and are dispersed in wet, muddy places where the amber snails live an amphibious life.

Some of the snails pick up the eggs as they browse on decaying leaves of marsh plants. The tiny parasites hatch out as swimming larvae, finding their way to particular lodgings inside the snails' bodies where they will be in a position to feed and grow without killing their host.

Each parasite produces a series of long maggot-like bodies during the life of the snail. When the right moment comes, the fully developed "maggot" elongates and contracts within one of the snail's eye-stalks with the instinctive intention of attracting the eye of a bird. When this purpose is fulfilled, the bird either swallows both the snail and parasite or else pecks the maggot from the snail's protruding eye. In the latter case the snail grows a new eye and its parasite grows a new "maggot". Once inside the bird, the maggot disintegrates and produces fluke worms.

I used a pair of forceps to simulate a bird's beak. When I made a peck at the pulsating "maggot" it recoiled and then thrust itself forward with more violent pulsations, obviously asking to be snatched from its prison. I then gripped its head firmly with the forceps and was able to withdraw it easily from the snail's eye. The snail, although temporarily blinded in that eye took little notice of the event and within a few moments was browsing gently on its leaf. I could see a second plump "maggot" already restless to escape from within its body. The name of this parasite is ***Distomum macrostomum***.

Terror on the Dyke Bottom

Norfolk 28/5/55

Water Scorpions are very common in local dykes. They are curiously flat, slow insects which sham death when they are pulled out of the water in tangles of weed. They are brown as peat and when lurking at the bottom among the dead remains of plants and mud they become almost invisible.

It is their habit to lie in wait for other aquatic insects and even such creatures as small tadpoles. These they seize suddenly with their pinchers, in the manner of a praying mantis. They are not really scorpions, but bugs. They suck the juices of their prey, much as plant bugs suck sap.

These creatures play a little at night, sometimes leaving the water to scuttle over wet grass, or even taking flight. They have well-formed wings and when these are outstretched a beautiful scarlet colouring is revealed on their backs. Although spending the greater part of their lives under water, they are air-breathers and must come to the surface at intervals to take in oxygen through their long tail-tubes. During the coldest part of the winter, they are able to lie snug and inactive in mud without coming up for air.

In May, one can find the eggs of these insects inserted neatly (often in rows) in soft, decaying stalks of water plants. The eggs are pinkish-buff in colour and shaped rather like millet seeds. Each is fitted out with a crown of ray-like filaments at one end and these are said to collect oxygen from the water for the developing infants. The young emerge looking much like their parents in general form, except that they are much lighter in colour and have only the rudiments of wings. They take about two months to grow up. In their youth they spend more time at or near the surface of the water than their parents, and I have seen them, and the young of their cousins, thegreat water stick-insects, preying upon young pond skaters. In July most of them are adult.

In the late summer they may often be found with numbers of small, bright-red parasitic water-mites fastened to their bodies. The mites do not kill their hosts, but fall off after a time and lead an independent life swimming freely in the water.

The water scorpions mate and lay their eggs in the spring and die soon afterwards. They lead such obscure lives and move so little by day that they rarely appear to be noticed and taken as food by birds or other animals.

Ferocious of Broad and Dyke

Norfolk Broads 22/2/58

The great diving water beetle (**Dytiscus marginalis**) is one of the commonest, liveliest and most ferocious insects inhabiting our Broads, ponds and ditches. The adult beetle is an olive-brown, boat-shaped creature, about an inch-and-a-quarter long; its sides are bordered with narrow lines of pale yellow and it has long, powerful, silk-fringed swimming legs which are superb, articulated oars. The male has smooth, polished wing cases; those of the female are nearly always ribbed lengthwise, but I have twice come upon smooth-backed examples in ditches near Yarmouth.

Males are distinctive in possessing large, golden-brown sucking discs on their forelegs and with these they clasp their mates while swimming. The insects rise to the surface from time to time to replenish their air supplies. The tail is exposed to allow air to be drawn in through two large apertures connected with special chambers and at the same time the wing-plates are lifted a little so that a coating of silky hairs beneath them may also trap a silvery film of air, to be absorbed later in the depths.

The divers are like living submarines. They lurk in the shadows, keeping watch with their multiple eyes, each of 9000 tiny lens, ever ready to make a sudden pursuit. They will attack almost anything that moves and enjoy a varied diet of caddis-worms, mosquito larvae, water snails, worms and small fishes such as sticklebacks. It is not unusual for them to savage larger fishes, as goldfish keepers discover to their sorrow occasionally. The sharp, curved, tooth-edged mandibles of the beetles are sufficiently powerful to draw blood from the tough-skinned fingers of a man and the soft belly of a fish offers much less resistance.

Sausage-shaped eggs are inserted by the female in slots in the stems of water plants during the summer. The eggs produce translucent, rather shrimp-like larvae equipped with long spindly legs and very large sickle-shaped jaws. These are veritable dragons. They seize and devour other creatures one after another and hardly ever stop eating during the six weeks taken to reach their full size. When they have become about two inches long, they crawl out of the water and burrow into the damp earth, excavating a roomy chamber in which pupation takes place. A new generation of beetles emerges in early autumn; but by no means all the old beetles die at the end of the breeding season.

A friend of mine kept a Dytiscus alive for five years and I had one for half that time, living in a jam jar, so it may be judged that these are among the longest-lived of all beetles. In their adult state, it is not unusual to find these monsters in difficulties a long way from water. It is their habit to undertake high flights by night from time to time and when the moment for descent arrives, the insects are apt to mistake glass roofs and shining car bonnets for water glittering below. So they come down with a ping instead of a plop, often stunning themselves.

Beetles on Fair "Dodgems"

Norfolk Broads 13/3/76

Even before the end of the winter, if the days are sunny, one can find whirligig beetles disporting themselves on the ponds and ditches. Small, black and boat-shaped, they move with the speed of quicksilver. Their backs are so shiny and waterproof that they reflect the light in bright points, while when they scatter and dive on being alarmed, they carry silver bubbles of air attached to their tails and continue to glitter in the depths. Sometimes they form large flotillas in the sheltered waters and are always gregarious, even when only two or three are present, darting about and bumping into one another like excited children on the "dodgems" at a fair.

During the colder months these insects hibernate in mud at the roots of water plants and hold reserves of air under their wings sufficient for their modest needs during the period of complete inactivity. At other times they occupy themselves inerratic display and pause from time to time to devour any dead insect which may be floating on the water; they are also said to take some nourishment from plants.

In May and June the females lay eggs on submerged vegetation. These produce slender, translucent grubs equipped with ten pairs of feathery gills for breathing underwater. The larvae feed on other insects to a great extent, but are partly vegetarian and, becoming full-fed in August, they leave the water to climb on the fringing plants and pupate in greyish cocoons usually camouflaged with fragments of floating litter.

A new generation of beetles emerges in early autumn, and like many other aquatic insects they tend to take wing and seek fresh hunting grounds on fine, calm autumn days. They make sizzling sounds of stridulation as they are about to take to the air and hum like bees in flight.

There are ten species of whirligigs, nine of which have been found in the Norfolk Broads district, two of the commoner ones even occupying salty ditches near the sea while some are seldom found away from the clear running water of streams. Oil pollution seems to have had a bad effect on populations in recent years and they are no longer as familiar a sight on our waters as formerly.

I wonder sometimes why the design of their highly-efficient leg paddles has not been imitated for boat propulsion.

Silver Beetle Beauty in a Ditch

Breydon Water 4/2/61

One of the most brilliant and beautiful creatures inhabiting the ditches of East Norfolk is the great silver water beetle, (***Hydrophilus piceus***).

This insect, much prized by people who keep aquaria, is now a rare and local species practically confined to southern England. It is favoured by fish-keepers because it eats water weeds and is not even partially carnivorous, so far as the adult beetle is concerned. Almost as large as a stag-beetle, often two inches long, it has a polished greenish black back and carries a glittering silver bubble of air held by yellow "fur" on its underside. Instead of rising tail-uppermost to the surface of the water to take in air, like most other water insects, it collects the air by using its small clubbed antennae like the mouth of a funnel, through which air passes to the bubble-holding hairs below.

About 30 years ago I had the pleasure of seeing several of these silver beetles in a slightly brackish, mud-lined ditch near Breydon Water. I kept one for a short while and remember being intrigued by its rather clumsy method of progress underwater. It could hardly be said to swim, but rather to crawl, even when it was not on the bottom, because its legs waddled along with alternating strokes instead of being used like oars, as in most other water insects. The beetles emerge in late summer and autumn and do not breed until the following year, usually in June. Then the females spin beautiful silken purses among the waterweeds, much as spiders spin cocoons, and place about fifty eggs in them, in strings. The larvae bite their way through the silk and disperse to feed and grow fat on water snails. They become three-inch long leathery grubs with rather small heads and in due course, usually in July of the following year, climb out of the water.

It is important that they should be able to find clay mud alongside the ditches, because their next step is to excavate neat spherical cells in the mud, inside which they eventually curl up and assume the pupal state. After a period of a little under three weeks the beetles escape to the water. They are pale and soft at first, like crabs changing their shells, but exposure to the air hardens their outer skeletons in a matter of hours. These large beetles often leave the water on warm summer nights and are attracted by lights. Many are seized by herons patrolling marsh dykes and their horny wing-cases are often found in pellets ejected by these birds, especially on the Halvergate marshes.

My friend, the late Mr P E Rumbelow, made a special study of the life history of these beetles at Southtown, near Great Yarmouth, and I enjoyed several opportunities of looking in on his experiments. These insects have proved rather elusive for most entomologists searching for them in Norfolk. When intensive surveys of water beetles in Broadland were carried out by F Balfour-Browne, in 1904-5, the silver water beetle was detected only in very small numbers in one area, near Barton Broad.

Water-Jet-Propelled

Wheatfen 21/1/78

The rove-beetles are a very numerous tribe. They include the rather large black "devil's coach-horse" common in gardens and noted for cocking its tail and assuming a threatening attitude when disturbed.

Most of them, however, are very small, some being among the insects classed as "thunder-flies", which get into one's eyes and produce a painful stinging sensation when encountered on a country walk or cycle ride.

All are characterised by their very short wing-cases (elytra) confined to the front half of the body so that the long, segmented abdomen trails behind. While a few are carnivorous, far more live as scavengers, frequenting manure heaps or feeding on decaying vegetation in the undergrowth. A good many of them attack fleshy fungi or browse on moulds. There are even a few which frequent seashores, burrowing in sand like sand-hoppers when the tides are high.

Numerous species of the genus **Stenus** abound in marshes and some of these can be found in sedgy and reedy litter all through the winter. On my fen at Surlingham, where at least 13 kinds occur, the commonest is **Stenus bimaculatus**. This is about 8mm long, with yellowish legs and two orange spots on the elytra, but otherwise dull black and somewhat downy, and it has large and prominent eyes. In times of flood, one finds an assortment of insects floating on the surface of the water, quite apart from pond-skaters and other species which live in that way habitually. **Stenus bimaculatus** is able to make the best of both worlds, because it is equipped for adventuring across water at will.

Whereas most terrestrial insects finding themselves adrift in a flood depend on the wind or swirling currents to carry them within reach of a drier haven, this beetle is able to straddle the water on tiptoe and propel itself forwards by squirting what appears to be an oily fluid on to the surface from a gland at the tail-end of its body. Thus it demonstrates the principle of jet propulsion in the true sense, revealing an aptitude for technical specialisation which has served its needs in all probability for a million years or more.

Thunder fly - *Stenus bimaculatus*

Escape From the Floods

Wheatfen 16/11/68

On November 4, 1968, a big tide in the River Yare welled over the banks and flooded not only the rond marshes of Surlingham, but also several of the roads leading to the riverside.

When this happens after water levels remain normal for a month or two the exodus of small mammals such as field voles, shrews and moles fleeing from the rising waters has something of the drama we have come to associate with the Kariba Dam episode. However, periodic floods of the river valleys have their uses for some small creatures, as well as for various marsh plants whose seeds are dispersed on the waters. Many insects are floated off mud and vegetation and carried to new living quarters when the floods rise.

On the recent occasion I noticed that the predominant insect voyagers on the waters over the marsh road near Coldham Hall were certain minute spidery flies whose wings were reduced to the merest frail vestiges so as to be quite useless for flight. Very few kinds of true flies (*Diptera)* have given up flying, so I was greatly intrigued by the presence of hundreds of these little skaters on the flood waters. They proved to be of a *Sphaerocerid* species, *Copromyza pedestris*, found dwelling in the depths of sedge litter on rare occasions.

Under normal circumstances these flies, which are only 3 to 4 mm. long, must be extremely difficult to detect in the dark, damp crannies which are their secret habitat. They are very bristly creatures, with red eyes. It may be that they can see better in the semi-darkness of their haunts with red eyes. Their clothing of hair no doubt assists them in floating on water. Some very similar flies (*Anatalanta*) live in the Antarctic.

Other wingless or very short-winged species occurring in Britain include *Braula,* a parasite of honey bees and a few hairy parasites of bats and birds; there are also a few other little marsh flies which sometimes develop short wings; but in *Copromyza pedestris* this feature is constant.

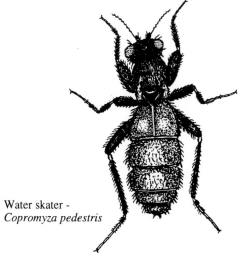

Water skater -
Copromyza pedestris

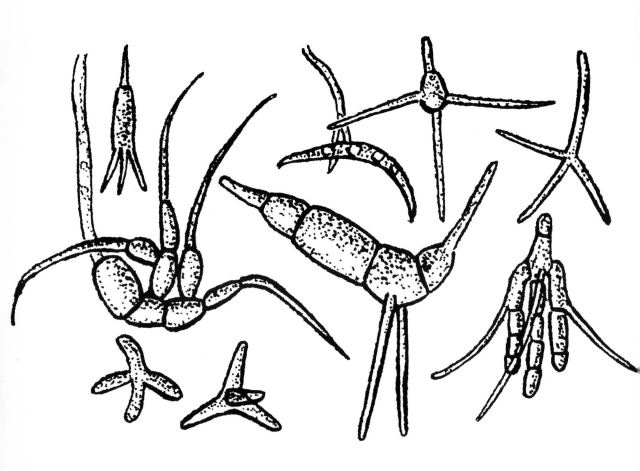

Spores of complex form – spidery, starry and sickle-shaped, and in some cases resembling shrimps or mosquitoes.

Grotesque Water Moulds

19/11/66

In autumn, when leaves drop from alders, willows and other water-side trees, many of them drift into streams and ditches and presently sink to the bottom. Once they have become immersed, they are apt to be attacked by a variety of microscopic animals which live by scavenging, while bacteria also set to work on their soft tissues as they rest on the mud and slime of older, decayed remnants of the leaves of other years. In the earliest stages of disintegration one finds great quantities of aquatic moulds developing on these newly-fallen leaves.

The spores of these fungi abound in fresh water, especially in well-aerated streams, and where the current is slow at bends and obstructions masses of such spores often form a pearly grey, almost iridescent scum which is apt to gather on the tips of over-hanging leaves and twigs and to form rippled silky-looking sheets where the water forms eddies at the approaches to culverts. Scores of different species of water-fungi are engaged in this business and their spores are of many elegant shapes. One feature most of them have in common is the possession of long arms and spines. These help to keep them in suspension in moving water by adding to their bouyancy, besides increasing their surface area likely to come in contact with food-holds; but their chief value would seem to be in increasing the chances of the spores getting caught on leaf-hairs and serrated leaf-margins as they drift along.

When the spores come to rest on a sunken leaf they put forth rooting threads of trans-parent mycelium.These penetrate the leaf-tissue and form thick bundles of strands in and about the mid-ribs and veins.Within a very short time the newly-established fungus colonies develop delicate stalks, often in tufts, bearing a succession of spores from the tips of their branches. In some cases the spores simply break free at the joints when they are fully formed: in other instances they are sloughed off by pressure from within the organs bearing them, like chains of bubbles issuing from a clay pipe.

Some spores are spidery, starry or sickle-shaped, but more complex forms occur, bearing resemblances to shrimps and even mosquitoes.

Drone-Fly Master of the Air

Wheatfen 4/12/76

In autumn, it is common for rather large flies resembling honey-bees to come into the houses and buzz around the lights when they are put on at night.

Sometimes the insects can be found hidden in the folds of curtains and behind pictures on the walls, while a visit to almost any loft or attic in the winter will probably result in their discovery in some numbers. They are drone flies (***Eristalis tenax***), so called from their superficial resemblance to drones or hive bees in size, colour and general markings, except that they possess only a single pair of wings. They neither sting nor bite and are harmless in every way.

Breeding all the summer in muddy places, they spend sunny days visiting flowers from which they take nectar and pollen like bees, though purely for individual consumption and not for storage, since they do not rear young in cells like bees and wasps. I have noticed that they often feed in a nicely regulated fashion. When first alighting on a flower, a drone-fly will suck pollen grains from all the stamens in turn and then delve deeply with its long proboscis to take a draught of nectar before passing to the next flower. Presumably it gives good service as a pollinator. On hot days one is likely to see these flies patrolling ditches and especially shallow puddles in a meaningful way, darting down and settling on the water's edge from time to time.

They are members of the hover-fly tribe and show themselves to be masters of the air during these exercises, sometimes keeping perfectly still in mid-air, especially when courting is in progress and the males are showing off their paces.

Their larvae are dingy aquatic grubs known as rat-tailed maggots and so named because they have long telescopic tubular tails which act as air ducts like those used by human divers (snorkels) before compressed air became available. A star-shaped nozzle at the tip prevents water being sucked in with the air at the surface. These maggots consume the nitrogen-rich waste in sewage and the drainings from farmyards, and are extremely efficient in their work.

Sometimes vast numbers of drone-flies cluster in caves and hollow trees for hibernation and could be mistaken for a swarm of bees.

Important Wartime Role

Norfolk Broads 16/11/57

In spring and summer, many brightly-coloured beetles with a metallic lustre on their bodies and wing-cases are to be seen feeding on marsh and water plants almost everywhere.They are abundant around the margins of our Broads and the riversides. They are "reed" beetles (***Donaciinae***), all of which spend the earlier stages of their lives feeding on submerged roots and stems of aquatic and reed-swamp plants.

Most of them obtain their oxygen supplies for breathing while they are under the water in a very cunning way. They tap air-filled spaces between the cell tissues of their food plants. The grubs make cocoons in late summer and connect these with the air supply before they assume the chrysalis state. After a short period, the perfect beetles are formed; but they stay inside the cocoons, which might be likened to diving bells all through the ensuing winter, waiting for the warmth and sunshine of late spring to tempt them forth into the upper world of greenery and flowers.

Different species are attached to reeds, water-lilies, pondweeds, sweet grass, burreeds, bulrushes, reed-maces, iris, cotton grass, marsh marigold and various sedges, and the adult beetles are to be found visiting many kinds of flowers, sometimes in very large numbers. Their colours range from pale gold, through to bronze, fiery copper, green and blue to violet.

One species found in Broadland is of particular interest, because it spends the whole of its life underwater. This beetle is ***Macroplea mutica***, variety ***curtisii***. It is a rare insect in Britain and occurs most plentifully in the slightly brackish water of some Broads and marsh dykes in East Norfolk, where the cocoons are to be found attached to the rootstocks of the common reed and sea scirpus. The beetles are active in May and June, when they crawl about, always submerged, among the thready leaves of the fennel pondweed (***Potamogeton pectinatus***). Their bodies are covered with a golden pile of very short, bent hairs, which hold a thin layer of gas, with the aid of which oxygen in the surrounding water can be utilised for respiration. This remarkable mechanism known as plastron has been perfected by very few kinds of aquatic insects, the best known of which is a bug which inhabits the River Wensum near Norwich.

The plastron underwater breathing apparatus was subject to intensive scientific study during the last war and yielded valuable new information in a highly important field of research. Norfolk was able to supply both the bugs and beetles needed urgently at the time of these studies and I remember with pleasure an officially blessed expedition to the home of ***Macroplea mutica*** alongside the Acle New Road, at a time when security measures restricting travel in that area were in force. Even a beetle can become a V.I.P. in wartime.

Clouds of Midges

North Wales 14/8/76

The boggy and mountainous regions of Scotland, Ireland and Scandinavia are notorious for clouds of midges which make life uncomfortable for people taking holidays in those areas. East Anglia, because of its drier climate, is relatively untroubled by these minute biting insects; nevertheless, we have some of them making a nuisance of themselves here and there in damp, grassy places.

Ranging from one to three millimetres in length, they have short beaks and scissor-like jaws for making incisions in the skin of people and even hides of horses. Their wings have cloudy patches and black spots and are folded flat over the back. The worm-like larvae may flourish in water, leaking tree-sap, decaying vegetable matter or mats of algae in bogs and salt-marshes.

Only the females seek blood meals, as in the case of mosquitoes, and they are most active when the air is humid, especially after light rain has been falling.

The larger animals are not their only victims; besides mammals and birds, caterpillars are attacked by some species, while there are extremely agile midges which manage to settle on various flying insects such as butterflies and even mosquitoes, to suck fluid from their wing-veins.

Once, in North Wales, as I was looking down from a bridge over a stream, I saw mayflies being attacked by biting midges which managed to land on their backs as they rose from the water. One kind of biting midge (***Atrichopodon pavidus***) devotes its attention wholly to nibbling pollen and the juicy tissues of certain flowers. It gathers in swarms on those of honeysuckle as they open on summer evenings. Both sexes are involved and mating takes place on the flowers. The insects, dusted with pollen, are very effective in bringing about fertilisation. I have also found them visiting yellow flag irises and regal lilies whose fragrance resembles that of honeysuckle.

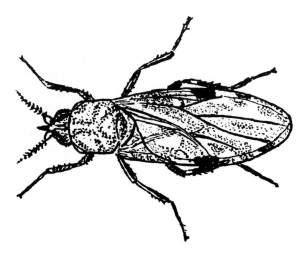

A midge that bites -
Atrichopodon pavidus

Spread and Decline of Fern

Norfolk 21/4/56

An exquisite little water fern, **Azolla filiculoides**, sometimes attracts attention on the surface of dykes and pools in East Norfolk, more particularly in the late winter and spring, when its fronds assume a fiery crimson tint.Earlier it has ablue-green colour and is often silvered with beads of moisture.

Under suitable conditions it forms floating carpets covering waterways completely. Its crinkled many-branched leaves are buoyed up by floats filled with air, so that they stand higher on the water surface than those of duck-weeds and floating liverworts. Spores ripening on the fronds in summer sink to the bottom and lie on the mud until the following spring, when they rise and produce new plants on the surface. In mild winters many of the old plants survive, but they are not very resistant to frosts.

Our Azolla was introduced to Europe from North America towards the end of the 19th century as an ornamental plant to be grown in aquaria and in tanks in conservatories. In this country, the first news of its escape into the open was given by a Mr T W Odell, who sent a note to "Science Gossip" in 1883, stating that it was then covering a large pond at Pinner, in Middlesex, and was already becoming established on several other ponds round about.

Its first introduction into Norfolk seems to have taken place in 1903, when some was grown in a tank in the Chapel Field Gardens in Norwich. In 1908 it was found by the late Mr F H Barclay to be covering a ditch on the Woodbastwick side of Horning Ferry.The notorious flood of 1912 broke up the Woodbastwick colony and scattered the floating plants over much of the Bure Valley. A year later, it was seen flourishing far afield: Ludham, South Walsham Broad, Stokesby and in the dykes on the Acle Marshes. By some means, it reached the Yare and was found abundantly in dykes connected to the river at Surlingham in 1916.

In 1921, it was seen in incredible abundance at Denver Sluice in Fenland, having floated dowwn the Ouse in thick carpets. Experience over the years has shown that it suffers in severe winters, becoming scarce as a result: but colonies survive here and there and it spreads again to redden the surfaces of pools and dykes with its crystal-like fronds.

This water fern once existed as a true native of Europe a few hundred thousand years ago and one of the exciting discoveries made by Dr R G West during his study of the Great Interglacial Lake deposits at Hoxne recently was of the spores of **Azolla filiculoides**. We may reflect that, like ourselves, palaeolithic man in East Anglia took pleasure in the crimsoning of galaxies of little fronds on the lake waters in season.

Water Soldier

Great Yarmouth 18/1/58

As a schoolboy I was fond of exploring the marshes lying between Yarmouth and Burgh Castle. On one of my early rambles during the winter, I stopped to peer into one of the deep main dykes on the Bradwell marshes and was thrilled to discover a sort of submerged garden of weird copper-coloured plants rather like tropical aloes or pineapple tops, with toothed leaves.

Such was my introduction to the water soldier, one of the most remarkable East Anglian plants. Later, I was to find that the plant rose to the surface and produced beautiful white flowers in summer, when also their crown leaves, emerging slightly from the surface, became a bright golden green and formed starry centres to the red-brown rosettes of older leaves. I never succeeded in discovering seeds, and now know that in these latitudes the seeds do not mature, because the fertilising male element fails to function. Further south in Europe, seeds are produced normally, but in the extreme south of the plant's range only the male element is active, and again there are no seeds.

The water soldier (a Broadland name for it is "pickerel weed"), Stratiotes aloides, abounds in many of our larger dykes and in some of the Broads, but has vanished from a number of its old haunts in recent years. It is rare in this country outside Norfolk. There is only one species of water soldier in the world today and it ranges over the greater part of Europe and just into north-west Asia. It is the last of a line which has been traced back nearly 60 million years in fossil deposits found in this country.

The present kind flourished here in Cromer Forest Bed times and left plenty of its well-formed seeds behind with those of hornwort and other water plants in the black peat. The fact that it seeded freely then suggests that the interglacial climate prevailing was similar to that found today between latitudes 52 and 55 degrees North (the present seeding zone of the water soldier).

Reproduction takes place in Norfolk waters by means of long-stalked buds whose stalks rot and release them in winter. It is believed that the plants sink at the end of summer as the result of accumulating an encrustation of limy matter on their leaves;presumably the ballast is shed to enable the plant to rise to the surface when the sunny season comes round again.

A large tawny dragonfly with green eyes, known as the Norfolk Aeshna because it is found in Britain only on the Broads, depends upon the water soldier to provide it with a highly specialised kind of home in early life. The discovery was made only a few years ago and it explained why the dragonfly had such a restricted range. This intimate association between a dragonfly and a water plant may well have been established many millions of years ago. Perhaps we shall find fragments of our Norfolk Aeshna in the Cromer Forest Bed some day.

Giving Broads a Jungle Look

Norfolk Broads 28/2/70

Quiet backwaters of the Broads are often fringed with tussock sedges (***Carex paniculata***). Sometimes hundreds of their shaggy tussocks, standing four or five feet high, dominate the black swamps and remind visitors of the sort of primeval jungles met with in tropical regions.

Norfolk marshmen call them "gnat-hills", possibly because gnats have a habit of dancing above them in smoky clouds in summer, and until fairly recently reed-cutters often used their long, tough leaves for tying bundles of reed. It was also an East Anglian custom to slice off the whole tussocks and dry them for use as hassocks in country churches.

These most graceful of sedges develop most commonly on quaking mires. As peat accumulates from their own decaying material the root systems rise gradually and new growth is seated higher and higher on the old remains, which soak up moisture from below like a sponge. Eventually, after a great many years, the tussocks may die suddenly in a very dry summer, but where they are perched at the waterside some of them become top heavy and fall over, whereupon the crowns gradually grow up again.

The tussocks wither and bleach very quickly when fens are drained. I remember that when Holkham Mere in West Norfolk was drained in the 1930s, thousands of these sedges stood like golden haycocks on the black, shrunken peat.

Round some of the Broads one finds a variety of marsh plants growing on the top of tussocks, including delicate marsh ferns, milk parsley, valerian, purple loosestrife, and even orchids. Quite often, seedling trees such as sallows and alders take root on the crowns and when this happens the tussocks are shaded out and rot away, so whole jungles of them give place to swampy scrub and eventually alder woods like Heron Carr, near Barton Broad.

Many creatures take shelter under the shaggy leaves. They are favourite couches for otters. Coypu lurk in them. Wild ducks, coot and moorhens use them for nesting, as do small rodents, shrews and even stoats and weasels here and there. In winter floods the tussocks are a refuge for vast numbers of hibernating insects and spiders and I have found peacock butterflies sleeping in them in the winter. Some marsh snails lay eggs in the peat just under the crowns. The tussocks remain partly green in winter and look their best in June, when the brown flower spikes are adorned with pale golden stamens.

Tussock sedge - *Carex paniculata*

Home of the Marsh Pea

Norfolk Broads 9/7/66

Here and there in the depths of Broadland's marshy jungles one can come upon scenes of rare splendour, especially in July when there is the greatest wealth of flowers and the richest variety of greenery.

I know niches in mixed reed-fens where at a single glance it is possible to capture a vision of every rainbow tint in blossoms and leaves; red of sorrel, orange of jewel-weed, yellow of Creeping Jenny, gold-green of fern, blue-green of sedge, blue of skullcap, amethyst of marsh pea and every delicate hue in the linking sequence, shining from the petals of loosestrife, orchid, bedstraw, valerian and bird's foot trefoil.

To a stranger visiting our lush swamps for the first time, the wild flower which usually has the greatest appeal is the marsh pea (or blue marsh vetchling as it was called earlier by Norfolk's famous botanist J E Smith, or marsh chickling vetch as it was known to the early 18th century botanist who found it growing at Ranworth. The delicate relative of the garden everlasting peas grows only in wet fens, where it scrambles to a height of as much as six feet, supporting its slender, winged stalks by means of three-pronged tendrils atthe tips of its compound leaves. Each stem gives rise to several well-spaced sprays of clear lavender-coloured pea-flowers in groups of two to six throughout July.

It flourishes best where there is a mixture of rank, unmolested marsh vegetation, including tall reeds and sedges which it can climb here and there. It seems to require moderately alkaline conditions, probably because these suit the nitrogen-fixing bacteria which live in its root nodules; it is absent from acid bogs. Formerly much more widespread in England, it has disappeared from a great many of its old haunts as the result of improved drainage, mowing and grazing.

Nowadays, like the milk parsley beloved of swallowtail caterpillars, it is locally plentiful only round the Norfolk Broads. Being a northern plant in Europe, it may well have survived here since very early times, braving a succession of ice ages, on the fringes of glaciers where summer melt water swamped the valleys. It seems to have very few natural enemies.

The marsh pea
- blue marsh
vetchling.

Black Swallowtails

Horsey 21/7/79

In June 1979, Anya Bertholdt and her brother found a rather tattered large black butterfly in their garden at Stable Cottage, Horsey. They took it to John Buxton for identification and it proved to be a melanistic variety of the swallowtail, which is extremely rare.

The first one ever recorded was caught in a landing net by an angler, Mr J H Lloyd, at Ranworth on August 9th, 1921, and eventually found its way to the Rothschild collection at Tring. This discovery excited the interest of collectors, who flocked to Ranworth and took no less than 17 specimens in the next 13 years. The variety must have flourished in spite of this onslaught and, happily, not everyone was imbued with the craze for collecting.

One old friend of mine told me that he often saw the odd black swallowtail visiting marsh flowers while he was fishing at Ranworth and on one occasion he saw six of them on one day. In the 1930s they became very scarce. However,I chanced on a magnificent velvety black specimen in pristinecondition, sunning itself on sedge beside Ranworth Dyke on May 17th, 1936, and saw another, in a somewhat tattered state at Wheatfen Broad in the Yare Valley on May 29th, 1944. Since then I have not heard of any further encounters until this summer's find by the children at Horsey.

It is good to know that the melanistic race has not vanished altogether in our wild population and the fact that most of the swallowtail's haunts in Broadland are protected as nature reserves nowadays provides some assurance of continuity.

The breeding of these freakish examples has been undertaken successfully in captive colonies and Dr E B Ford found that the black coloration was carried by a recessive gene. When mated with typical examples, the blacks produced only offspring of normal coloration, but when mated with one another produced a small proportion of black ones.

It must be very exceptional for black to mate with black in the wild, but this may have happened very locally at Ranworth in the 1920s, so giving rise to a temporary abundance of these black beauties. Nowadays the British race of the swallowtail flourishes only in fens surrounding the Norfolk Broads, where its caterpillars feed on milk parsley and angelica. Flying in sunny weather, chiefly in June and July, it shows a preference for visiting pink and purple flowers, perhaps its greatest favourite being ragged robin.

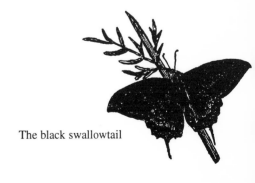

The black swallowtail

Fragrant Water Mint

15/9/73

Water Mint is a very common plant in water-meadows and the more open parts of our East Anglian fens. All through the summer its leaves yield a fragrance rather like peppermint, very noticable and, in fact, dominant as one walks across marshy ground. From mid-August to the end of September the pale lilac-coloured flowers, bristling with stamens, appear in rounded terminal clusters. They are very attractive to bees, especially honey bees, and to various butterflies.

For centuries the sprigs of this plant were used in this country to make infusions for refreshment and medicinal purposes. It was also customary to strew this mint on floors of churches and in halls on the occasion of feasts, in the same way as sweet flags and lady's-bedstraw were used in the Middle Ages, when life in towns tended to be dominated by unsavoury odours.

Although wild populations of this species (**Mentha aquatica**) have on the whole remained stable in character and restricted to wet habitats, hybridisation has occurred on a number of occasions with other mints commonly grown in gardens. Our best-known garden species is the spear-mint (**Mentha spicata**), with the smooth, bright-green, rather jagged leaves and narrow flower spikes, which do not have projecting pinhead stamens. This is the plant which makes the most popular mint sauce to go with mutton, and its scent is sharp and clean, without the peppermint sweetness. When it is crossed with water mint the offspring include the peppermint of commerce, infinitely superior to the marsh-dwelling parent.

In the same mongrel brood we find sundry other forms which are now in cultivation because their scents have a curious interest for us. One has the scent of eau-de-cologne and another a lemon-like odour so that it can be used for flavouring sweet dishes. Once an attractive hybrid has been produced it can be propagated freely by the division of rootstocks, which can be relied on to make vigorous growth year by year. The spear-mint is also one of the parents of some of the broad-leaved forms, both hairy and smooth, which are excellent substitutes for it for sauce making and cooking with new potatoes. Several of the hybrids mostly found by chance originally by discerning herbalists have been in cultivation for as long as we have any botanical record.

Fragrant watermint -
Mentha spicata

The Beauty of Parnassus

Norfolk 1/9/62

The ivory-white chalices of the grass of Parnassus stud Norfolk's rushy fens in autumn like emblems of purity. They stand out brightly, like small, neat lilies on long stalks, with the amethyst cushions of flowers of Devil's scabious for company and in a green setting of bog moss on some of our wet commons.

Called Parnassus by the ancients, because of their startling beauty and supposed origin on the hill of that name where they were believed to have sprung from the earth by a miracle, they have the same spell-binding charm for flower lovers today. Their cups have a glistening perfection, an air of waxen fragility, enhanced by a delicate veining of the petals and, coming late in the year, they recapture for us the magic of early spring in their bright virginity. Like their relatives the saxifrages, they are self-fertile, the stamens bending over one by one to shed pollen by touch on the central stigma.

They set multitudes of very small seeds in the rounded capsules which swell after flowering. There is need for this great provision because most of the seedlings are doomed to be overshadowed and crowded out by competing marsh vegetation in due course. As it is, Parnassus has vanished from most of its old haunts in southern and central England during the present century and here in East Anglia, where a sturdy reserve holds on, its population has diminished greatly since the regular mowing of Broadland marshes and fens ceased early in the 1920s. July mowing used to favour this species, because tall competitors such as meadowsweet and rank grasses were removed, allowing smaller flowers to burgeon late in the season.

In the northern moorlands and in Ireland, where there is not much tall vegetation, Parnassus is much more plentiful and safe, although it tends to disappear when bogs are drained. It has few despoilers. In the north, but not with us, I have seen its light green leaves parasitised by the orange clustercups of a rust-fungus which goes on to attack sedges. In the south this rust has a similar association with wild currants, stinging nettles and sedges, infecting one and then the other in regular alternation.

Homes of Many Insects

Norfolk Broads 7/3/70

Reed beds are the home of many peculiar insects which in turn provide food for specialised marsh-dwelling birds such as reed warblers in summer and bearded tits at all seasons.

The shoots, leaves and stems are inhabited by the caterpillars of several species of wainscot moths; root-stocks harbour grubs of reed beetles which tap their air supplies underwater from the plants' vascular systems; flat chinch-bugs swarm in the leaf-sheafs and take their fill of sap throughout the summer. Conspicuous features in this community are the plump, cigar-like galled shoots produced by the larvae of a slow-moving fly, *Lipara lucens*. The adult fly lays eggs in young shoots in spring, with the result that further elongation of the stem is arrested and a swollen, leafy bud develops. The fly grub occupies the core and eventually pupates in the gall chamber, so that with luck a fly of the next generation creeps out from the top next year.

During the winter the galls remain in position, where they run little risk of flooding, but when the reeds are cut there is a tendency for the galled shoots to snap and fall into the stubble, so that regular harvesting of the reeds does not entirely eliminate the population.

Where the reeds remain standing from year to year the galls usually survive for a second season and after they have been vacated by their original occupants they are commonly taken over by some remarkable little black bees, *Prosopis pectoralis* . A female bee enlarges the exit and proceeds to pack pollen and nectar into the thick-walled cavity. She stuffs the whole gall with a series of food-packs, laying an egg in each and separating the packages with wads of chewed reed. In the following spring, male bees emerge first from the upper cells and females from the lower ones.

Reed-cutters are only likely to come across the bee-inhabited galls where harvesting is undertaken in alternate years, ("double-wale"). Because the reeds are older and therefore more fragile by the time the bees are in possession, the galls are apt to fall clear during mowing operations and this gives the occupants a fair chance of survival.

This is not the whole story. Reed-galls provide homes for at least 25 different species of insects, including specialised "guests" and many parasites – some being parasites on the parasites.

Reed gall residents - *Lipara lucens*

I Wrote Notes by Glow-Worm Light

Corfu 27/6/81

In the 1920s, I spent many a summer night savouring the enchantments of a dewy world: the fragrance of honeysuckle and sweet briar, the churring of nightjars, the trilling of natterjacks and the hooting of owls.

Nothing delighted me more than the glow-worms twirling their tail-lamps as they climbed grasses to attract the winged male beetles in several fenny places which I was in the habit of visiting in Lothingland. On good nights, I could count 100 or more in view at once and, by placing a few on a sheet of paper, I was able to write notes by their light. These insects were at the time plentiful on many of our wet commons and around the Broads; but they have since vanished from much of our countryside and even where they still hang on, numbers are generally small. I suspect that a major cause of their decline has been the attraction of the winged males by lights.

As long ago as 1893 the Norfolk coleopterist James Edwards recorded that he had found male glow-worms swarming at night about the lamps at Brundall railway station.

When I first came to live at Surlingham in 1946, I found that scores of these beetles came to the lights in the house. There are still glow-worms in my fenside garden, but they have disappeared from the adjacent marsh banks where they used to abound. It seems that the concentration of putative husbands near a light source explains their local persistence. The snails and slugs on which they feast are as widespread and plentiful as ever in haunts deserted by them in recent years, but now the magically luminous insects linger in only a few of their former haunts.

In May, 1981, I was able to fulfil my ambition to see fireflies flashing their lamps in flight among the olive groves of Corfu. The larvae of these insects (***Luciola italica***) closely resemble those of our glow-worms, being black, with orange markings. The males, unlike ours, flash their signals which are answered by the females below.

Glow-worms and fireflies swarm in tropical forests in many parts of the world and sometimes assemble to give displays like fireworks round certain trees. I have seen a firefly fossilised in a piece of Baltic amber, showing that these insects were flourishing in northern Europe more than a million years ago.

Night Revels of a Surprisingly Agile Slug

Wheatfen 21/9/57

Slugs play an important part in breaking down vegetation at the end of the summer. This is because so many of them reach their full size at that time and feed voraciously as they are preparing to lay their eggs. The effects of grazing by enormous numbers of slugs are specially noticable in some of the Broadland fens in September and October, when most of the tall herbaceous plants and even the marsh grasses are denuded of their leaves, late flowers and even their seed-heads by milky marsh slugs (*Agriolimax agrestis*).

I have seen these slugs by torch-light on autumn nights, slipping about the foliage gracefully like skaters showing off their paces on a rink. A single plant of wild angelica or milk parsley may be attacked by 50 or more. The creatures glide up the stalks to the flowering and seeding umbels and to the tips of the leaves and in their eagerness do not hesitate to plunge headlong over the edges. In falling they are held safely by threads of slime as strong as the life-lines spun by spiders; moreover I have seen them climb their threads to regain footholds on the leaves after having dropped as much as eight inches.

Of all the British slugs these are the liveliest nocturnal revellers; until one has seen them disporting themselves under ideal conditions, in mild, moist weather on a still autumn night, two or three hours after sunset, one would find it difficult to believe that slugs could be so agile and carefree in their movements.

Agriolimax agrestis is a native of northern Europe. In this country it was not identified with certainty anywhere until 1940, when it was found to be living in great abundance in the Yare valley fens at Surlingham. Since then, it has been ascertained to have a wide distibution in Broadland and this summer I was able to confirm its occurrence in Scotland. It is a cream-coloured slug, reaching a length of just over one and a quarter inches when full-grown and its slime is milky due to the presence of lime.

Its nearest relative is the far too common field slug *Agriolimax reticulatus*. This is sometimes the same colour, but is more often a deeper buff or dusky with brown and black streaks and mottlings. The fen slug is comparatively smooth, slender and streamlined; the other is noticably wrinkled on the back, more thickset and with a species. Each has humpy mantle.There are also internal anatomical differences between the two a small hidden shell; that of *agrestis* is incurved on the right-hand side and that of *reticulatus* is convex. The field slug is far less active than its relative of the fens. The two also differ in their breeding habits. The common kind breeds all the year round; the other only in autumn. One mystery concerning these two slugs has yet to be solved. Although the field slug inhabits marshy places as well as fields and gardens almost everywhere, it does not seem to share our East Norfolk fens with its relative, but stays on higher ground. Yet it thrives in the fens of Cambridgeshire and Huntingdon, where the true fen slug has yet to be discovered.

Norfolk Weeping Willows From Napoleon's Tomb?

Old Lakenham, Norwich 26/3/77

James Grigor, in his "Eastern Arboretum", 1841, extols the virtues of the weeping willow as a tree to be planted in gardens by the water and makes mention of several fine specimens to be seen in Norwich and its neighbourhood.

He makes particular mention of a fine example growing at Sprowston Lodge and states that it was grown from a slip brought from St Helena in 1823 by Captain Lucas of the East India ship Lord Amherst. I have heard the story many times that Norfolk's weeping willows came from Napoleon's original grave in St. Helena and there is no doubt that weeping willows grew there, almost certainly introduced from France, where it was common practice to plant these trees in churchyards.

Exactly how and when these graceful trees originated is something of a mystery, however. Some botanists believe that they all stem from a chance hybrid which arose through the crossing of **Salix babylonica** with the golden vitellina variety of the common white willow, while others regard them as merely a sub-variety of the golden willow.

Nearly all willows show a tendency to hybridise rather freely with one another, so providing many puzzles for botanists, but this was not known when Sir James Smith described a number of these forms as distinct species, largely from the collection grown at Old Lakenham, near Norwich, by James Crowe, at the beginning of the 19th century.

One point of interest which should be borne in mind when considering the status of our now-common weeping willows is that the light green leaves and catkins appear on their pendulous golden wands in March, whereas those of one of their supposed parents sprout a month or more later in spring. Their other peculiarity lies in their production of both male and female flowers on the same tree, sometimes in the same catkins, whereas it is normal for willows to have male and female flowers on separate trees.

I think there can be little doubt that every specimen now growing in Britain originated from one tree and some certainly from Napoleon's tomb. What would Nelson think of this turn of events?

Weeping willow - *Luciola italica*

59

Willow Ermine Moth Caused a Stir in 1930s

Waveney Valley 1/6/57

In the summer of 1936 hundreds of white willows in the Waveney Valley were stripped of their leaves by the small speckled caterpillars of the willow ermine moth (***Yponomeuta rorella***). The damage was so extensive and spectacular that it attracted wide notice. Many of the trees were completely defoliated and their branches and trunks became festooned with vast shrouds of greyish white silk forming the communal webs of tens of thousands of caterpillars. Local authorities took steps to control this new insect pest in East Anglia, but a plague of the caterpillars occurred locally in the following summer.

Although the moth was not recognised here until 1936, a Beccles entomologist, Mr E T Goldsmith, recalled that he had seen similar caterpillars on willows near the town, in comparatively small numbers, from 1931 onwards, so it seems likely that the original invasion was on a small scale and that the population increased gradually until it reached plague proportions which attracted popular attention.

In early August, 1937, large numbers of willow ermine moths swarmed onboard the Outer Dowsing light vessel, 30 miles off the Norfolk coast, proving that the insects could extend their range effectively by long flights on an intensive scale. From 1938 onwards the caterpillars were found on willows throughout Broadland and in West Norfolk and the Fens; but no real plague seems to have occurred since 1937. Many of the insects fell victims of parasitic ichneumons when they were most abundant, and it is possible that real biological control was effected by this means. I am not even sure that the moth is still with us; I have seen no sign of webs on white willows anywhere in the past five years. The moth is certainly not a regular immigrant from the Continent; nor was there any record of its being troublesome in this country before 1936. Until then, it had been regarded as a rare and local insect confined to Sussex and Dorset.

Another little ermine moth very similar to this species in general appearance, but with slightly darker wings, used to be generally common along the country hedgerows, where its colonies of caterpillars sheeted the hawthorn bushes with their webs. This insect was also to some extent a pest of apple trees in some areas. It seems to be comparatively rare with us nowadays.

In Germany, during the Hitler regime, innumerable thorn hedges were cut down by edict of the land planners. Until then the little ermine caterpillars had been common on the bushes, but not significantly so on fruit trees; but following the removal of the hedges they became a major apple pest within a few years. Whereas the apple had been a second choice, the insects were forced to make it their only food plant and thereafter became accustomed to it as their normal host, so that a phenomenal increase followed. There are other insects which can attack our fruit trees, but fortunately retain a slight preference for hawthorns. So there is something else to be said for the preservation of hedges in the countryside.

Fragrant Shrub of Peat Fens

Broadland 28/4/84

Sweet Gale, also known as Bog Myrtle, flourishes on many of the deeper, wetter peat fens of Norfolk's Broadland and on the grassland bogs near the Wash. Otherwise, it is rather scarce, with a very patchy distribution in eastern England, but it abounds on Scottish moors and western Irish bogs, much of Lakeland and North Wales, where a wet climate favours it.

A small deciduous shrub which subsists, like alder, with the help of bacterial root nodules, in acidic situations, it bears rust red-brown catkins in showy profusion on its still-leafless branches in April. Normally, the male and female flowers occur on separate plants, which have the odd habit of changing sex from year to year, while in old age both types of flower can be found side by side on the same individual. The fallen catkins are commonly exploited by an elegant little cup fungus (***Ciboria acerina***) which reaches maturity just at the time a fresh crop of catkins is being shed in spring. Strangely enough, this fungus was not detected in Europe until I discovered it in Yorkshire and Norfolk in April, 1945.

The willow-like leaves are dotted with fragrant, glistening yellow glands whose sweet, resinous flavour is noticeable in the mutton where sheep graze moorlands spriggy with this shrub. The powerful scent does not deter insects from attacking the foliage, which is stripped by small caterpillars in summer, while those of several large moths also make inroads, along with beetles, including one special weevil which feeds on nothing else. The leaves often appear brown-spotted above where a startling white parasitic mould is shedding spores from the underside. The dead twigs also harbour a special snow-white crystal-covered little cup fungus of their own.

Bog myrtle has been used for laying away with clothes, like lavender, to keep away moths. The leaves give a pleasant spicy flavour, used in moderation, like those of bay and rosemary, when boiling ham. We have also found that a sprig or two infused in making wine from birch sap adds appreciably to its bouquet. On the whole, however, the pleasant essences of sweet gale have been largely unexploited through the centuries.

Cup Fungi Gain Place in the Sun

Broadland 22/3/58

Many of the most extraordinary creatures in the world are parasites, and naturalists never cease to wonder at the complicated arrangements whereby they exploit not only one, but often a series of different kinds of hosts in turn, in fulfilment of their needs. In many cases, while adventuring from one host to another, the chances of making the right contact are so slight that it is necessary for their reproductive units to be launched in astronomical numbers in order to ensure the perpetuation of the species.

Their life-cycles are often most beautifully and cunningly adapted to the seasonal activities of their hosts. While living at the expense of others, they must keep their demands within reasonable bounds, since it would be fatal to them, as well as to their benefactors, if claims were pressed too far. So they are above all masters of adjustment and, as such, provide the student of plant and animal evolution with some of the knottiest of problems.

Parasitology is a science in itself today and it has been found that the best approach towards an understanding of complex examples of parasitism is through the study of border-line cases. In fungi, for instance, some species ordinarily subsisting on dead wood may, under certain circumstances, become parasitic on living trees.

At the opposite extreme there are some of the plant rusts, which are obligate parasites, accustomed to infecting one kind of host in spring and another quite different type of plant in summer and autumn. For instance, the barberry leaf rust goes on to attack grasses, including wheat.

As an example of a border-line case of parasitism, I would mention a charming little cup fungus, *Ciboria amentacea*, which is now showing itself in dark, moist leaf-litter under alder trees in the marshes of Broadland. The light brown cups, up to half-an-inch across, emerge into the sunlight from their sodden bed between February and April every year. When extracted with care, they are found to be connected by slender stalks up to two inches long with old, blackened male catkins which dropped from the trees in the previous year. The catkins have not decayed, because they have been mummified by the fungus living in them.

The alder leaves falling in autumn have covered them with a soft carpet and, because of this, the cups must be thrust up on stalks just enough to ensure that they shall gain a place in the sun. The cups expand, filled with ripening spores, just when the new catkins are trembling on the boughs above. Presently, as the glory of gold and crimson fades from the alders, the spent catkins fall to the ground. Many of them drop on the Ciboria cups which, at the slightest touch, scatter their spores into the air, like puffs of smoke. The new catkins are thus claimed and utilised by the new generation, at no direct expense to the alder trees. Male catkins of grey sallow are exploited occasionally by the same fungus; **Ciboria acerina** deals with those of bog myrtle, **C. aschersoniana** seizes upon the fruits of sedges in our fens and **C. batschiana**, producing large brown cups in autumn, preys upon acorns.

Great Migration of Camberwell Beauty

Snettisham, Norfolk 1812/76

1976 will be long rembered by entomologists as the year of the Camberwell Beauty. The history of this butterfly's occurrence in Britain has shown that spectacular immigration on the scale just experienced takes place only once in a century. We have to go back to 1872 to find records of a similar grand visitation, when not less than 150 specimens were collected in the east of England and a great many more were seen all over Norfolk and elsewhere.

This year some of these butterflies reached nearly every county in the British Isles during August and September, the greatest number appearing in Yorkshire, with Norfolk also receiving a large share of the visitors. Everything points to the source of these migrants being in Scandinavia, where there is a flourishing population of them, the caterpillars feeding on birch and willow chiefly in the mountainous forest country. Under normal circumstances this species is not migratory and one can only presume that just once in a while it responds to a stimulus of exceptional atmospheric conditions by embarking on mass irruptive expeditions.

Unfortunately, so far as this country is concerned, all invasions by these butterflies prove abortive. To hibernate successfully they need deep and prolonged winter cold. Our climate is not severe enough to ensure their survival until the spring, when they are due to mate and breed. As the next Ice Age approaches, however, the time should come when they will colonise Britain successfully.

Following the massive immigration of 1872, a single Camberwell Beauty survived up to January 5th, when it was seen to fall out of a tree at North Creake. Since then there have been no records of the butterfly having been observed here in winter until this year, when Mr L T Hall and his son enjoyed a close view of one at Snettisham on February 26th.

Following the big influx of August-September this year, I have received no word of any of the insects having been sighted in the country, but it is possible that some are attempting hibernation in hollow trees, thick with ivy and the like. If for once our winter proves very cold there is just a chance that a few of these lovely butterflies will survive and perhaps even breed naturally somewhere in Britain for the first time.

Royal Fern Excels in Norfolk

Norfolk Broads 21/6/58

Some of the largest specimens of the Royal Fern (***Osmunda regalis***) to be seen anywhere in Great Britain grow in Norfolk. Here, they flourish in alder carrs close to several of the broads of the Bure and the Ant valleys and scattered clumps occur even in open situations where peaty land extends to the coast dunes at Horsey and Somerton. The finest plants form great tussocks six feet high, with a spread of seven or eight feet, and I have measuredindividual fronds five feet long.

The stools have masses of black roots and are nested with bleaching red-brown fronds of past seasons. The outer leaves are sterile and those in the centre bear green feathery spikes of "flowers" which release clouds of glittering spores from mid-June to mid-July. It seems that these spores require very special conditions for their germination. Young plants appear only on the surface of slightly acid peat which is in partial shade, but not heavily overgrown with tangled vegetation and where moisture is always available but flooding occurs only for short periods.

The sporelings never develop successfully in fens which are swamped by river waters containing lime and for this reason the strongly-tidal Yare Valley today produces no young royal ferns in the alder and sallow carrs fringing its broads. Although two magnificent clumps transplanted to a ditch side at Surlingham from Ranworth in 1918 have produced millions of spores annually, not a single youngster has sprung up in the vicinity, which is rich in other kinds of ferns.

Once established, it seems probable that an Osmunda is capable of existing for centuries under favourable conditions; but even in the absence of interference by man, many things can happen to bring about the death of such a plant, poised at the brink of land and water and in the hinterland between sunshine and deep summer shade.

This species has suffered greatly from human interference in East Anglia and many of the colonies known to botanists in various parts of Norfolk in the 19th century have become exterminated as the result of land reclamation and in some case because people have dug up the plants, to peddle them on market stalls. Osmunda fibre is used extensively by orchid growers, but supplies of this mostly comes from abroad.

The fern has a very wide distribution, being found in Europe, Asia, Africa and both South and North America. It is not very frost-hardy, and is not able to exist in the Arctic, nor in those parts of Europe and Asia which have a markedly "Continental" climate. We find the remains of old rootstocks of it in the early interglacial forest bed at Mundesley, where its presence provides a clue to the type of climate prevailing while it flourished. I hope we shall long cherish this most glorious of ferns in Broadland so that those who follow us may share the pleasure of seeing its summer green and autumn gold.

Fishing for Shrimps in Norfolk Chalk Wells

Norfolk 30/10/71

During the many millions of years living creatures have existed on earth, animals and plants have become diversified to exploit a very wide range of habitats, in many cases adapting themselves to extremely challenging circumstances. From the sea's deepest abysses to the frozen peaks of the highest mountains, animals have managed to conquer the environment, both physically and behaviourally. Springtails flourish with lichens in the Antarctic, firebrats brave the heat and fumes of vocanic craters and there are midges which breed in oil wells.

There are also many hundreds of animal species which have found refuge and a special way of life in the bowels of the earth where light never penetrates. Explorers of deep limestone caverns in various parts of the world have discovered a rich fauna of blind creatures, including crustaceans up to the size of small lobsters, flies, mites and even pale, translucent salamanders.

In East Anglia we have no swallowholes and tortuous caverns traceable to great depths, but in the subterranean waters of the chalk there exist some small living relics of past ages, notably colourless crustaceans known as well-shrimps. From time to time these shrimps are noticed in water supplied by artesian wells, but very few have been investigated thoroughly by naturalists.

Their presence in Norfolk was first noticed by Sir Sidney Harmer in 1899. He identified two specimens from a well at Cringleford, known previously from chalk wells in the south of England. Doubt has been cast on this identification in recent years because no further examples of this species have turned up in any part of Britain which, like Norfolk, experienced the full impact of prolonged ice ages. In recent studies undertaken by Brigadier E Glennie, several Norfolk chalk wells have produced the closely-related **Niphargus kochianus** ,which appears to be more widely distributed than **N. aquilex**.

The usual method adopted for obtaining these shrimps from the depths is to lower an open bottle, baited with cheese or fish, attached to a nylon line on a fishing reel. The bait is left down the well for a few hours and the bottle is then brought very gently to the surface. A few years ago I accompanied Brigadier Glennie when well shrimps were obtained at Barnham and Litcham, but there has been very little such sampling undertaken in the region and there may well be interesting surprises in store for those who widen the search in the future. (In 1977, some were found in a chalk well at Houghton Hall.)

Black Puffball 1000 years in a Roman Well

East Wrentham Heath 30/3/74

Near a clump of pines on East Wrentham Heath this week I noticed what looked like a black, diseased apple lying on the sandy turf. It was rather like one of the black, rounded crampball fungi often seen sprouting from dead ash trunks.

When I went to pick it up, rather gingerly, I found that it was neither of these things. It turned out to be a featherweight object, for a start, and this at once helped me to recognise it as a sort of puffball, namely ***Bovista nigrescens***, which has a very smooth black, parchment-like skin when ripe and contains masses of purple-brown spores and fluffy threads. In my specimen there was a ragged hole at the top and flaps of skin had been rolled back from two other rents lower down. The fungus was not attached and appeared to have been rolled and bounced across the open breckland heath by gusts of wind, until it arrived in the shelter of the pines.

These particular puffballs used to be fairly common on pastures and rabbit warrens but one seldom comes across them since there is very little permanent grassland in which they can persist nowadays. Happily some stretches of grass-heath are preserved in Breckland and while the sandy turf is grazed by sheep and rabbits one can expect ideal conditions for propagation of black puffballs to persist. In the past these species of ***Bovista***, like the giant puffballs which occur in hedge bottoms in late summer, were much in demand (in their dry state) for staunching wounds in man and his domestic animals. The name of ***Bovista*** is a latinised form of the Norfolk term Bull-fiest used for certain puffballs.

A short time ago I was asked to investigate a mysterious object found in a Roman well in our area. It turned out to be a ***Bovista nigrescens*** whose skin and spores were still recognisable after having lain buried for well over a thousand years. Whether the puffball had been blown into the well or was dropped by someone who valued its medicinal purposes we shall never know. (Well-preserved specimens of this fungus have been found in excavations of prehistoric dwellings in Orkney and Northumberland.)

A Curling Earth Star

1/11/83

The rivers of Norfolk and Suffolk are flanked for much of their lengths by terraces of gravel and sand left there by the outwash of glaciers during the periods of climatic amelioration. These deposits nowadays yield vast amounts of material for use in building and road making.

Their excavation has revealed not only bones of various wild mammals which roamed our countryside and have become extinct in the course of time, but also caches of flint tools left by prehistoric peoples. When the mining comes to an end, we are left with a series of pits in the valleys, many of which become filled with water and provide habitats for aquatic birds, fishes and plants and facilities for recreation, while it is inevitable that some become repositories for rubbish. Before this disturbance on a major scale was initiated in our time, the valley sides were clothed with vegetation.

Two hundred years ago, T J Woodward, from his home at Bungay, made a number of interesting botanical discoveries in that part of the Waveney Valley. He was notably successful in finding curious fungi known as earth stars on the sandy banks there, some proving new to science. I have often wondered why this area was so rich in these fungi which although associated with well-drained, sandy soil, in most instances also require lime which is normally leached rapidly from sand, through the percolation of rainwater.

In 1983, I found the answer. When visiting a derelict gravel pit at Wortwell, I came upon a quantity of one of Woodward's earth stars on a steep, sandy slope partly over-shaded by ash and spindle. The ground vegetation consisted of ground-ivy, a few nettles and a patch of dog's mercury. This complex of vegetation provided evidence of an adequate supply of lime and I soon discovered the source. It was in the form of numerous little pebbles of hard chalk included in the gravel spilled there among the flints preponderant in the glacial outwash. Thus the needs of the exceedingly rare little hygroscopic earth star *Geastrum recolligens*, first described as a distinct species by Woodward, were still being served adequately.

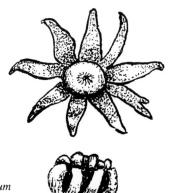

Earth Star - *Geastrum recolligens*

'Dreamy' Fungus Danger to Young

Norfolk 6/2/82

Relics of ancient civilisations in Mexico include many inscriptions which show that the eating of the "magic mushrooms" was a common feature of religio-mystic ceremonies indulged in by the indigenous people of that country.In the colder regions of Europe, Asia and North America, from very early times, the scarlet flycap has been widely exploited for the purpose of frenzied intoxication on festive occasions. It is only recently, however, that eating hallucinogenic fungi "for kicks" has come to be indulged in in this country, along with the growth in the pernicious habit of smoking cannabis resin and a sadly evident increase in drug addiction generally.

The fungus chiefly involved here is the Liberty Cap (***Psilocybe semilanceata***), a rather small toadstool with a pale yellowish, markedly pointed cap and a thin, milk-white stem, the whole tending to become tinged with bluish-green when stale after gathering. The gills and spores are purplish-black. Because it flourishes very commonly in grassy places all over Britain, including lawns, there is no practical means of preventing access to it. Nor would any attempt at suppressing it by chemical control have any real chance of success, except temporarily here and there, since airborne spores abound everywhere and re-establishment after treatment would not be long delayed.

Doctors in some areas are having to deal with sizable numbers of young patients suffering ill-effects through eating Liberty Caps. To the young, "forbidden" fruit tends to have a special attraction and experimenting in dangerous fields will always be a lure for them. It is tempting to gain entry into the dream world of lotus-eaters and magic mushrooms contain drugs which produce a sense of well being in those who nibble them. But as realities fade from consciousness leading to schizophrenic behaviour, the foolishness of this indulgence becomes all too clear.

The victims of this adventuring reach our hospitals, adding unnecessarily to the burdens of their hard pressed staffs. So let the youth of Norfolk, at least, beware this particular method of addling their brains, poisoning their systems and aging them prematurely.

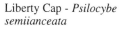

Liberty Cap - *Psilocybe semiianceata*

Lichens Help Monitor Atmosphere

Norfolk 25/3/78

Many of Norfolk's country churchyards have as yet escaped the radical treatment by which others have been deprived of their traditional interest and by well-meaning but unimaginative seekers of plain tidiness.

May the spirit of Gray's Elegy continue to haunt these ancient sanctuaries, for they have become rich indeed with the passage of the years, not only in the human interest of their crumbling memorials, but also in the variety of their wildlife. The study of lichens in recent years has revealed that, like the canaries which used to be taken down the mines to give warning of the presence of lethal gases, they are highly sensitive to sulphurous pollution of the air. Headstones in churchyards are commonly encrusted by these lowly plant forms, and so provide a widespread means of monitoring atmospheric changes year by year, especially when the same, often very long-lived colonies are inspected repeatedly. It is essential that the stones shall remain standing where they were placed originally, because their orientation conforms to a standard pattern every-where.

It is usual for lichen growth to be much more in evidence on the east-facing surface of the slabs (mostly limestone). I was puzzled by this, but think the reason may be that the dampness of night lingers while the morning sun shines on that side and conditions have become drier by the time the afternoon sunstrikes the other side. The contrast is of course greatest in summer.

Usually a headstone will be found decorated with a variety of lichens, which may be white, grey, dark brown, yellow, orange or red. These develop spreading rosettes, often dotted with spore-bearing organs of the fungi involved in a symbiotic relationship with the green or blue algae embedded in their structure.

Careful inspection reveals that different species compete with one another for living space, some inhibiting the growth of their neighbours when contact is made at the edges. The assortment is poorest in towns because of air pollution, but a few resistant species survive. Near the sea, the growth of these plants receives a boost from minerals drifting some way inland in sea spray.

Goldcrests and Firecrests

2/11/63

Year after year, in November great numbers of goldcrests move out of the coniferous forests of Northern Europe as the harsh Continental winter approaches. Some travel towards Spain and the Mediterranean and many cross the North Sea to reach the coast of East Anglia.

These smallest of all European birds are familiar to fishermen, who know them as "herring spinks" and the tiny visitors often swarm on board drifters out on the herring grounds on foggy and overcast nights. It is a great marvel that so many of them should achieve the sea passage successfully. They are tired out when they reach our coast and I have found swarms of them resting in garden hedges at daybreak after a big "rush". It is not uncommon for them to find their way into bedrooms in coast towns on autumn nights. I myself have awakened to find a goldcrest searching for spiders in my bedroom (at Gorleston) and one which I discovered in a garden shed one morning alighted on my head and explored my clothing as it might have searched the bark of a tree for insects. These birds, bred in the lonely forests, show no fear of man.

They spend much of their time in the company of various titmice while they are here in winter, flitting like little acrobats among the boughs of conifers and other evergreens and finding scale-insects and insect eggs. They are much attracted by cypress trees, from which they appear to obtain some resinous material. They attract notice by squeaking thinly and tremulously all the time as they move about, but they are not conspicuous in their soft, greenish plumage and one only catches sight of their gleaming yellow crests occasionally.

Some remain to breed here, building pendulous nests of moss and spiders' webs at the tips of fir and yew branches, but they are rather secretive in the nesting season and their snug litle homes are not easy to discover. The closely-related firecrest is a much rarer passage migrant and winter visitor here, but turns up in small numbers along our coast and in Breckland from time to time. It can be distinguished from the goldcrest by the clear white stripe above the eye and a black stripe running through the eye itself. Cock goldcrests sometimes have crests as fiery orange in colour as those of firecrests, so brilliance in this respect is not enough to go upon. Firecrests are usually much whiter underneath and the adult cocks have lovely gold-green patches just behind their cheeks.

Firecrests have been seen with increasing frequency in eastern England during the last few years. They do not thrive in Scandinavia, like many of the goldcrests which visit us, but live more in central and southern Europe, so we tend to be rather off their winter escape route.

Almond Darling of the French

12/2/83

Winter Heliotrope (**Petasites fragrans**) has become a widely familiar plant of shady roadsides and wastes in Norfolk during my lifetime. Its roundly hoof-shaped leaves differ from those of its relative, coltsfoot, in lacking points and angles and innot being white-felted beneath.

They are to be seen throughout the year, and from December to March they are accompanied, except in the most shaded situations, by spikes of loosely-clustered brushy heads of pinkish-mauve florets, speckled with dark maroon-coloured stamens. A sweet almond scent fills the air where they are growing, especially when the days are mild in winter. Believed now to grow truly wild only in Sicily and Sardinia and undescribed botanically until 1800, it became a darling of French horticulturists, as a pot plant sweetening the drawing rooms of Paris within a few years of its discovery. Importation into England, for similar use, soon followed and, like the aspidistra, became popular early in the reign of Queen Victoria.

It was also planted around shrubberies and received much admiration until its capacity for getting out of hand became only too evident. Spreading quickly with the help of underground shoots, it smothered all ground vegetation with its perpetual leaf carpets. Then as a troublesome weed, it became an object of eradication, resulting in its roostocks often being dumped in waste places. Sometimes, although cleared from gardens, it had already spread to adjacent verges and survived there.

In the present century it has become established somewhere or other in most of our towns and villages. Its spreadhad been wholly by vegetative means, because the introduced stock consists of male plants and no seed is produced. If the original plants grown here had been of both sexes it might now be very much more rampant in our countryside, having proved well able to endure all the vagaries of our climate.

The flowers make pleasant winter posies, being much used in this way in some parts of Europe, though not commonly here. On sunny days they may attract hive bees which venture forth for a winter airing and various hardy flies obtain refreshment from them. It would not be surprising if some of the moths which are on the wing in the winter also visit them.

Winter Heliotrope -
Petasites fragrans

71

Snowdrop Drifts

24/2/73

Great drifts of snowdrops delight the eye in many of our Norfolk woods and plantations nowadays, especially where the land is moist, while they are also widespread in grass near country houses and have found their way on to marsh banks and road verges here and there.

Nevertheless it seems almost certain that they are not true natives of East Anglia or even of the British Isles. Our 16th century botanists and herbalists reefer to them always as purely garden flowers introduced from Continental Europe and they were not even known as snowdrops in those days, but as "white bulbous violets". Their spread in Norfolk has been most spectacular since early in the Victorian era.

The name "snowdrop", though appropriate in every way, is said to have been derived from their similarity to the ear-pendants in fashion among German ladies at one time and known as "schneetropfen". Although Europe has twenty species of these flowers, only one (***Galanthus nivalis***) has become common with us. It is somewhat variable, however, and we often meet with "double" varieties and less often, flowers with yellow instead of green crescents near the tips of their inner "petals".

In recent years one other species has been introduced fairly widely: the large and broad-leaved ***Galanthus elwesii*** which has three bands of green on its "petals". The flowers are quick to respond to early winter warmth and may appear at any time from Christmas onward, though most commonly in February. Their nodding form not only helps them in pushing up through snow, but ensures that the organs of fertilisation are protected from damp and frost.

They are visited by early insects of several kinds, including honey bees in bright weather. They yield plenty of nectar and I have found that some of them are quite strongly scented. The plants die down and vanish quickly when warm weather comes in spring, but for some time afterwards one can find the ripening fruits lodged in the interstices of grass tufts, where the seeds are spilled to work their way down into the soil in summer.

The bulbs are said to be somewhat poisonous, but they are so deeply seated as to be well out of reach of grazing animals. Where the plants are bruised through trampling when they first come up they are apt to be destroyed by a grey mould. Otherwise they have few enemies.

Norfolk's Wild Daffodils

Norwich 18/4/70

Wild Daffodils (**Narcissus pseudonarcissus)** flourish in only a few of East Anglia's damp woodlands and meadows.   In some places they owe their presence to deliberate introduction by landowners in the past, but there seems to be a fair likelihood that they are truly indigenous within a few miles of Norwich in a district embracing Seething, Alpington, Bergh Apton and Claxton, where a number of scattered colonies exist in a pattern which suggests that they may have a relict native status.

These dwarf "Yellow Crow Bells", as they used to be called long ago, stand only about six inches high. Their nodding blooms are about two inches long with rich butter-yellow crinkly-edged trumpets scarcely longer than the pale-yellow perianths. The leaves and compressed stalks are slender and of a glaucous green colour contrasting with the yellower green of the meadow grasses. They are usually the first daffodils to open in spring and in the milder western parts of England they may be found blooming before the end of February.

Like crocuses, the flowers last only a few days as a rule, probably because they very quickly set seed, unlike some of the bolder hybrid forms in cultivation. They also manage to retain their characteristics unsullied by cross fertilisation by garden daffodils which may be growing nearby. This is very noticable in some of our country churchyards where masses of wild daffodils brighten the turf adjacent to the grave-mounds.

They appear to have great stamina and I have yet to see a plant blighted by any of the commoner diseases of cultivated daffodils.

By flowering early, they usually manage to ripen their seed and wither before much grass mowing takes place in spring; this is important for their survival in good fettle over the years. Since all daffodil bulbs are known to be somewhat poisonous, the growth of these flowers in pastures has been discouraged to some extent in the past and doubtless this accounts for their absence from many parts of the country. However, it is virtually unknown for livestock to come to grief through eating the bulbs, since these are deeply rooted, so there is really no good reason for banishing these plants which are such a joy to behold in the early spring.

Wild Daffodils - *Narcissus pseudonarcissus*

Primrose Sprites

Norfolk 10/4/54

The first spell of warm bright weather in April heralds the appearance of furry bee-flies known as primrose sprites (***Bombylius major)***. Like miniature humming birds, they dart and hover on invisible whirring wings just touching down on flowers with the tips of two legs (either fore or aft) while the long proboscis is inserted for the extraction of nectar.

Their bodies are golden brown and they have rather prominent beady eyes. As their common name suggests they find primroses, including the polianthus in our gardens, specially attractive; but their attentions are by no means confined to those flowers. I have seen them visiting periwinkles, bugle, bluebells, lungwort (Adam and Eve), apple blossoms and Japanese quince. But they seem to take no interest in buttercups, dandelions or any of the legumes such as gorse and broom, nor do they join bees at pussy willow catkins.

Their mimicry of small, furry bees suggests some association with these insects and indeed they have evolved a parasitical way of life dependent on the mining bees which tunnel into sandy banks and lawns. The female "sprites" are able to locate the bee colonies in spring when their breeding activity is at its height and new brood cells are being made and furnished with stores of pollen and nectar.

They may be seen hovering over the ground where the bees are busy and showering down their eggs in flight. These eggs produce minute worm-like larvae which endeavour to creep into the bees' tunnels and enter as yet uncapped brood cells. They then remain inactive long enough for the bee grubs to develop and attain sizable proportions, whereupon they feast upon the fattened prey and in due course pupate within the cells as usurpers.

When spring comes, the fly pupae climb out of their cells with the help of a crown of stiff spines and wait, with their tops just protruding from the ground surface, for a warm day to prompt the liberation of the adult insects.

Oak's Banded Acorns

Dilham,Norfolk 11/11/73

A remarkable oak tree bears black-banded acorns in the parish of Dilham. It is a common pedunculate oak and only freakish in this one respect.Local people used to say it was brought as a young tree from the Crimea and planted by General Windham, but one of the vicars of Dilham recorded that it was a well-grown tree in 1872, and must therefore have been introduced more than 18 years previously.

In 1912, when it was judged to be about 70 years old, the girth of the trunk, measured five feet above field level by W H Burrell, was 6ft 4in. In 1966 the girth at the same eight was 8ft 6in, and in the last seven years this has increased a further 8in.

The banded acorns, according to all accounts, are usually on the small side. Those measured by Burrell in 1912, ranged from 10 to 13 by nine to 10 millimetres. This year (1973) they are a good deal larger, ranging from 15 to 30 by 15 to 17 millimetres. So it is clear that size is influenced by local conditions which vary from year to year.

It has been asserted on various occasions that this tree is unique in Britain. Does any reader know of another producer of ring-striped acorns?

In a paper to the Norfolk and Norwich Naturalists' Society in 1912, the Rev M C H Bird referred to the outstandingly heavy crop of acorns borne by Norfolk's oaks in 1911. An acorn competition held at the Stalham and Brumstead School yielded some interesting statistics.The local crop averaged 57 to the pound, which allowed them to be almost twice as heavy as "official" records had indicated. (The normal was supposed to work out at 125 to the pound). One monster specimen weighed nearly one and a quarter ounces. The longest acorn measured 42 millimetres.

From time to time oaks yield heavy crops, in some cases over a ton per tree. Acorns used to be much valued as food for livestock, especially pigs. This autumn, (1973), in my woods, wild creatures have lost no time in gleaning them from under the trees. They are appreciated by wood pigeons, rooks, jays, pheasants, wood mice, rats, squirrels and rabbits, while small birds often pick up bits of acorns crushed by traffic on the roads.

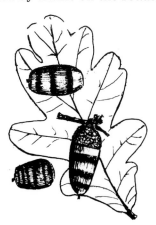

Banded acorns

Bird's Nest Fungi

Norfolk 28/11/67

Bird's nest fungi, so called because they look rather like miniature cup-nests containing clutches of creamy-white eggs, may be found growing on bare soil, garden rubbish and decayed wood, especially in the autumn.

One of the more conspicuous species, is ***Cyathus striatus***, which sprouts in clusters up to the size of a fist on very rotten twigs and boughs embedded in the damp leaf mould of woods. I find it most commonly on elm in Norfolk, but in some parts of the country it abounds on old, half-buried pine cones and sticks. On the whole it seems to prefer rather gloomy habitats.

The cups of this fungus are dark brown and shaggy on the outside and beautifully fluted and of a lustrous bluish-white tint within. On first opening, their mouths are closed with a creamy-white membrane, which becomes gelatinous and is dissolved to reveal several whitish "eggs" in the hollow. These eggs are packed with spores similar to those of a puffball and each sphere sits on a tightly coiled gelatinous thread attached to the inside of the cup.

In rainy weather, the cups become filled with water, which eventually loosens the eggs until they rise to the top and float.At this stage a large drop of water splashing down into the cup is likely to displace the egg and fling it to the distance of several feet. When this happens, the coiled thread is carried away with the egg and because it is gelatinous, it tends to stick where the egg happens to fall.

Now and again an egg becomes attached, temporarily, to a passing animal such as a hare or rabbit and so reaches a destination farther afield. Wherever it becomes lodged in the end, its disintegration is a slow business, because the skin is tough and only breaks to release the spores as a result of much wetting and drying alternately in the course of changing seasons.

Once a colony of ***Cyathus striatus*** has become established, it tends topersist for several years, continuing while there is enough nourishment available in the rotten wood to produce an annual crop of fluted cups from the basic mycelium or "spawn". Some other bird's nest fungi which grow on rotten straw are ephemeral, because the material they exploit decays very quickly.

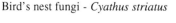

Bird's nest fungi - *Cyathus striatus*

Bracket Fungi Make Decorations

Norfolk 20/2/60

In the Tropics, especially in the great rain forest belt, there are few kinds of fleshy toad-stools. Possibly this may be due in part to the deep shade of the jungle, or to the presence of such vast numbers of insects that anything softly fungoid would be devoured before it could reach maturity. On the other hand, it may be a matter of the high temperature and humidity being unsuited to the agaric method of reproduction. Even in our own climate, it is not in the heat of summer, but in autumn, that most toadstools appear.

The nearer one approaches the Equator, the more woody fungi one finds, bracketing tree trunks and branches, some of these resembling enormous saddles in shape, while a great many are thin and frilly. Instead of gills underneath, they have numerous narrow pores which rain down spore powder when they are ripe.

We have a number of these bracket fungi in our own woodlands. Some are well known killers of pine, birch, elm, plum and so on, but most of them are saprophytes, developing on dying or dead twigs and stumps. One of the commonest of these harmless species, **Coriolus versicolor** .In general form and texture it is like a great many of the tropical jungle polypores. One often comes across its brackets, tier upon tier of them, beautifying a dead tree stump or forming a succession of frilly collars on a fallen branch.

Those who make a hobby of collecting natural objects of quaint shapes for inclusion in table decorations, often make use of the attractive **Polystictus**. It is banded with various colours like an ornamental fan, and the upper surface is like velvet in parts and has the sheen of satin in other zones. The colours may include violet, blue, crimson, gold, white and green; rarely, one may find a grey and black specimen, equally beautiful because of the silvery sheen on top.

Samples of this fungus are to be found in woodland glades at all seasons, because the brackets are tough enough to withstand a year or more of weathering. They are seen at their best in winter, however, after rapid growth during the autumn. In spring and during the summer they are apt to be ruined by fungus-beetles of various kinds, including a shiny, scarlet-and-black ladybird-like insect (**Endomychus coccineus)**.

It is possible to cultivate the ornamental **Polystictus**. A simple method is to cut a few stakes, such as are used as bean-poles, and insert them to a depth of about a foot in the soil. Place fragments of the fungus on the ground close to the stakes in late autumn or winter. A white mycelium will develop and invade the wood at and below the soil level and in due course, tiers of decorative brackets will appear higher up. Almost any kind of wood will do, but ash, birch, hazel and alder tend to yield results sooner than, for example, oak.

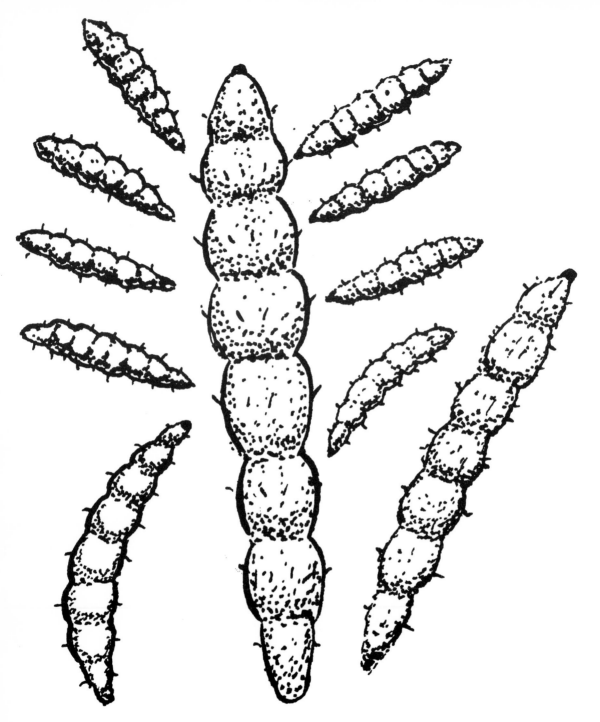

Great wonders of the insect world - the *paedogenetic* larvae of Miastor midges, remarkable for reproducing themselves while still in the maggot state and without mating.

Parent-Eating Maggots

Heydon 14/10/67

Now and again, when I am turning over rotten logs and branches lying on the ground in damp woodlands, I find groups of small white maggots arranged to form elegant patterns on the underside where there is a growth of moulds or creeping fungi.

Sometimes the maggots are clustered in heaps like miniature chrysanthemum petals or small ones may be grouped in circles, radiating like the points of a star from a larger grub seated in the middle. When I first came across a colony of these creatures, in a wood at Heydon many years ago, I was greatly mystified. As it happened, they prove to be one of the greater wonders of the insect world.

They were what are known as "***paedogenetic***" larvae of Miastor midges, remarkable for reproducing themselves while still in the maggot state and without mating. The "mother" maggots, on reaching full size, develop about 30 eggs, which hatch out inside their bodies.

The young ones gradually devour their parent from within and then emerge to browse on fungi coating the damp surface of the rotten wood. The daughter larvae grow large and multiply by the same process, and in the course of several successive generations the original "mother" may give rise to a maggot colony of several thousand strong.

This form of reproduction continues in suitable habitats throughout the autumn winter and spring, but when warmer, drier weather comes, the "mothers" produce a final batch of larvae which look slightly different from those which have appeared earlier; they are distinguished by possession of a breastbone-like ridge underneath. These assume the chrysalis state and, in due course, turn to midges.

All the offspring of one parent maggot are of one and the same sex, but both male and female midges occur as the end products of different "mothers". After mating, each female midge lays a very few monster eggs and the process of intensive larval multiplication begins again.

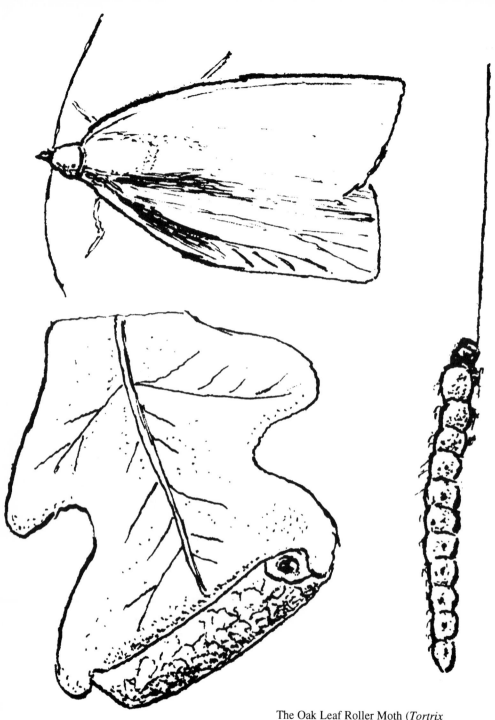

The Oak Leaf Roller Moth (*Tortrix viridana*) and its caterpillars, which strip the tops of young oak leaves towards the end of May.

Moths Plague Oaks in May

12/3/83

Foresters attribute the stag-headed appearance of many oak trees to the periodic plagues of the oak leaf roller moth (***Tortrix viridana)*** whose greyish, black-dotted caterpillars only too commonly strip the tops of their young leaves towards the end of May.

The moth, which has emerald green fore-wings covering the grey lower ones when at rest, is quite small (measuring at the most ¾ in wing span).

It flies in June and July, gluing its minute, flat eggs to the twigs and covering them with a sticky fluid, dusted with powdery scales from its wings. These eggs remain dormant all through the summer and ensuing winter and the infant larvae emerge just as the new foliage is sprouting in spring.The caterpillars begin to devour the tender leaves and flowers and make homes for themselves by curling the leaf edges downwards and fastening them to form cylindrical tubes.

The heaviest infestation occurs on the crowns of the trees initially, but when the branches are stripped in that region, the caterpillars descend on silken threads to ravage those lower down. In windy weather, many of the caterpillars tend to become airborne on their threads like money-spiders. During the war, I was called to identify masses of caterpillars found to be blocking the airspeed indicators of Mosquito aircraft coming to land at a Norfolk air base and they proved to be of this species. However, wind and heavy rain may also shake the caterpillars out of the tree tops so that they fall to the ground.

There is an avenue of oaks at Henham in Suffolk where I and others have seen black-headed gulls from the nearby Blyth estuary feasting on these caterpillars on the road towards the end of May. As a result, some of the gulls are killed by cars at this spot every spring, the crops of the victims being found to be crammed with these caterpillars. Titmice and chaffinches eat large numbers of these pests at this time, but make little impression on the vast numbers present in some seasons.

Defoliated oaks put forth new leaves on "lamas shoots" later in the summer, but these tend to become whitened with a powdery mildew (***Microsphaera alphitoides)*** and the overall growth of the trees is small in plague years, while the acorn crop is much reduced.

The growth rings revealed in cross sections of oak trunks provide evidence of plague years.

Weevil's Skill

Wheatfen 10/5/78

When walking in deciduous woods in early summer it is not unusual to see portions of green hazel leaves, rolled like cigars and hanging from what is left of the mid-ribs of the remains of living leaves. I have often examined these green "cigars" without being able to discover their makers in residence, although it is known that more than one kind of weevil is in the habit of treating leaves in this way.

Recently, however, I came across some small, rather shiny black weevils (***Deporaus betulae***) on hazels in my wood at Surlingham and one of them (at about 5.30 a.m.) was busy, very slowly and delicately, helping to curl the final fold of a rolled-up leaf with its feet and beak. The insect was only 4 mm. long and looked hardly strong enough for its curious task. No doubt it was helped by the relatively thin and pliable condition of the young leaf which was being subjected to this treatment.

The operation begins with the beetle cutting across the blade of the leaf with its exceedingly small, sharp jaws. Even the veins are severed, except for the mid-rib which is cut just sufficiently to almost stop any flow of sap and yet remain as a basal attachment for thedangling portion, which, although withering somewhat, does not dry out altogether and turn brown.

Further operations are carried out on the network of veins in the dangling part of the leaf so that the curling is facilitated. No silken threads or other insect secretions are used to fasten the folds, but punctures are made at intervals allowing the leaf's own slightly sticky sap to act as some form of holdfast preventing the rolls from unfurling.

Minute eggs are laid in the central hollow and the beetle grubs in due course nibble the green leaf blades hidden from sight of insectivorous birds and protected from the drying winds and heat of summer. Only the female weevils concern themselves with this elaborate scheme for the benefit of their offspring, but the males remain in attendance. Oddly enough, the males look more powerfully built than their energetic wives and can be distinguished at once by the massive thighs of their hind pair of legs (as shown in the illustration). The same species also makes "cigars" from the leaves of silver birch.

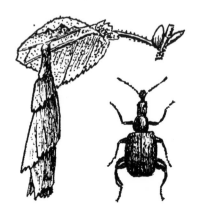

Shiny black weevils -
Deporaus betulae

Insects Which Cry Aloud When Alarmed

Keswick Hall, Norfolk 4/12/54

Frogs shriek when they are pursued by stoats, shrews or cats, and rabbits squeal when frightened, although they are silent at other times. It is not generally realised that some kinds of insects also cry out when they are alarmed. When I handled a death's head hawk moth which had emerged from a chrysalis this autumn, it squeaked loudly, like a startled mouse. The caterpillars and even the chrysalis of this insect are equally capable of emitting squeaks when jolted.

My first experience of this kind of thing was in 1927 when, on a winter's day, I happened to turn over a rotten log in the woods at Keswick. In dislodging a piece of bark, I disturbed a militant-looking beetle known as *Cychrus rostratus* and was taken aback when it uttered several wheezy squeaks in a rapid crescendo and diminuendo. These noises were repeated when I held the insect between my fingers and I could see that the sounds were produced, not from the mouth, the wing-shields or any stridulating legs, but by swift pulsations of the abdomen. It seemed that air was forced through the spiracles, or breathing tubes, to produce the squeaks.

I have handled other kinds of squeaking beetles since that time. The so-called "locust-beetles," which attack popular trees squeak like rusty hinges when they are picked up. These, like the magnificent musk beetles found occasionally on sallow bushes in East Anglia, produce sounds from special stridulating organs situated on their backs. Imms, in his Insect Natural History, mentions that the underground grubs of dor-beetles and those of stag-beetles in rotten wood also make stridulating sounds, by rubbing their legs together. A friend once told me that the giant black water beetle *Hydrophilus piceus* squeaked in a peculiar way, but I have never been able to confirm this.

Insect music can be both charming and maddening in warmer climes than ours. Our only shrill cicada is a small species living in the New Forest. We are familiar with the grasshopper stridulations in summer, the high-pitched chirpings of the house crickets and the jiffling music of bush-cheeps in the autumn dusk, but the sounds are soothing rather than piercing.

Very occasionally, I have heard the sizzling love-calls of small water boatmen on ditches. These insects "sing" to one another with their front legs. I am inclined to believe that my ears are no longer capable of picking up the songs of the water boatmen. The short frequencies of the sound waves produced by insects cannot be discerned as one grows older. One ceases to hear bats squeaking, then bush-cheeps seem to be silent; lastly, when we are very old, there are no skylarks for us.

Nightjar deserting East Anglia

East Anglia 7/6/58

I can think of no more enchanting experience than that of listening to nightjars churring softly in a pine wood clearing on a warm June night. These long-winged, owl-like birds of dusk and darkness used to take up residence every summer in almost every part of East Anglia where there were fern brakes, heaths and stretches of sandy country dotted with pine and birch trees, but since the end of the 1920s fewer have come back to us from their winterings in Africa and most of their old haunts are deserted.

We are at a loss to understand why they have diminished in numbers to such an extent; they are not persecuted, there are still places to attract them, moths and beetles on which they feed still abound and it does not appear that they are especially prone to fatal attraction by lights at sea during migration. If disease has been the cause, we have so far failed to discover the evidence of its prevalence, although one Norfolk ornithologist many years ago reported that he had found nightjars parasitised severely by worms.

These birds are remarkable in many ways. Their plumage is beautifully camouflaged to resemble lichen-patterned bark and they perch lengthwise on boughs so that the streaks of their feathers run with those of the bark. Two (rarely more) mottled pebble-like eggs are laid on the ground, most commonly among gorse or pine needles, and the hen broods over them all day. Her plumage is of a mixture of browns and blacks and buff, with irregular pencillings and woodcock barrings, so that she is almost impossible to detect as she crouches, with eyes shut, expecting to be mistaken for a piece of dead wood.

She comes to life in the gloaming and the cock relieves her of nest duty while she speeds away to catch her supper of crepuscular moths and cockchafers. Late in June when the chicks are being fed is the best time to visit nightjar haunts. Then one hears not only the prolonged churring of the cocks on their perches, but also the loud wing-clapping that is a feature of renewed courtship, together with the short growls of the toad-like young and the tack-tacking of the excited hens. If there is moonlight the birds will be seen gliding and circling like giant swifts among the trees. At times they float slowly, like patrolling owls, which they resemble to some extent in possessing very soft plumage.

In this part of the country they have been known commonly as "dor-hawks" for centuries past, "the hawks of sleep-time". They open their mouths widely and catch quite large moths, also numbers of cockchafers and buzzing black dung beetles. Another traditional name for the nightjar is "goat sucker" and this has been translated into the Latin name **Caprimulgus** for the genus to which most nightjars belong.

There is no evidence for the goat sucking, and I can suggest that the idea arose when goatherds of the olden days saw the birds wheeling about the animals where dor-beetles congregated, as they do in the summer dusk round the heads of people as well as beasts moving across open heaths and grassland.

Small Deer Settled in Norfolk

Norfolk 3/3/79

Since the late 1960s, two species of miniature deer have colonised Norfolk and become very numerous. Both can be said to have become firmly established in a few favourable habitats. In each case their presence stems from the escape of stock of Chinese origin kept at Woburn Park in Bedfordshire, at the beginning of this century, since when feral animals have spread fairly extensively in south-east England. In some instances, new centres of distribution have been established through the escape of animals kept in captivity elsewhere, such as Whipsnade and various wildlife parks.

The species most commonly met with in Broadland is the Chinese water deer. There are no antlers in either sex, but the bucks have two canine tusks protruding conspicuously from their mouths, those of the does being somewhat shorter. Their backs are light brown in summer, becoming somewhat greyish in winter and the large ears, held erect when the animals stand on the alert, are white inside, contrasting sharply with the blacknose. The tail in this deer is very short and the hoof-prints are about equal in the two halves.

The water deer tends to frequent rough grassy and rushy places and feeds by grazing. It has appeared increasingly in the Bure and Ant valleys in recent years, especially at Catfield, Horning and Hoveton and is now present also along the Yare, including Rockland and Surlingham marshes. This winter has driven some out into the open in a starving condition. Those on the north Norfolk coast may have fared better.

The equally diminutive Muntjac, which is more of a forest animal, delighting especially in thick cover, seems to have been more successful in colonising West Norfolk including Thetford Forest and the country around Hillington and Castle Rising, but there have also been a few penetrating the eastern side of the county. The bucks are easily identified by their very short, backward-sloping antlers based in long sheaths, with a pair of black lines forming a "V" on the forehead. The reddish-brown back, foxy in summer, becomes very dark in winter. The tail is fairly long with a white flash underneath and the hoof-prints are equal in their two sections. There are no exposed tusks.

Casual observers have often failed to distinguish these two species in the field and I hope that this short illustrated account will help to increase the accuracy of future recording.

Chinese (above) and Muntjac deer.

"Gas" Attacks by Caterpillars

6/8/60

The extraordinary caterpillars of the puss moth (***Cerura vinula***) develop to their full size during August, usually on leaves of white poplar, which they devour at a great rate. They may also be found on some of the other populars (although very rarely on aspen) and on various willows and sallows from time to time.

When sitting still they are well camouflaged, even when large, by their leaf-shaped silhouettes, including the tail spike, which resembles a broken-off stalk, and by their green colour, which is broken up by fold-like edgings of white or yellow and artificial shadows of purple and black.

When aroused suddenly, however, they become transformed into alarming creatures, with faces rather cat-like in front view and spiky tails raisedand projecting like stings, simulated by red threads which squirm and lash about in a way calculated to unnerve any bird and even a human intruder.

One also notices a strong smell of formic acid when the tail threads are extruded; this substance is manufactured by the caterpillars of both the Puss and Lobster moths for defence and it is a highly effective weapon. Although never actually injected into the enemy by a true sting, there must be occasions when it acts rather like tear-gas at close quarters.

When full-grown, the caterpillars imprison themselves in extremely hard cocoons of silk reinforced with chips of bark and sawdust and cemented into cracks in the tree trunks. The chrysalids are thus surely protected against the worst of the winter weather and the beaks of all birds except possibly the great spotted woodpecker.

How then can the moths break free from their almost stone-hard sheaths when the time is ripe? They have no teeth for cutting or sawing their way out. They produce caustic potash from their bodies and soften the cement cocoons; then with heads encased, they use the fore part of the bullet-shaped chrysalis as a ramming or bulldozing tool and so reach freedom.

Caustic potash is a substance used commonly by zoologists for "clearing" the bodies of insect specimens of fatty matter to reveal the chitinous skeletons, and it seems extraordinary that any insects should be able to flood its surroundings with such a chemical without running the risk of dissolving its own tissues. It is also astonishing that a caterpillar producing a lot of acid for defence should later in its development manufacture a strong alkali for another purpose.

The adult puss moth flies in May and June. It has a wing-span of about three inches and a very thick furry body, greyish-white with ermine-like black spots. The wings are white with numerous narrow streaks and cross lines of grey, tinged slightly with brown.The caterpillars are apt to suffer from the parasitic ichneumon wasps and in some years a bacterial disease wipes out many of them. Although there are so many willows and poplars in East Anglia, the Puss Moth can hardly be considered to be a common insect, except locally. In my experience, it is most often met with along the coast.

Caterpillars With Poison Hair Defence

11/8/73

Fluffy, snow-white moths about an inch long can often be found clinging to bushes, posts and fences during the day at this time of the year (August).

If the tips of the wings are parted gently, it will be seen that the hooded tip of the body is clothed with yellow fluff and it is this which distinguishes this species from a few otherwise rather similar but rarer relatives.

This moth is known as the Yellow-tail or Gold-tail (***Euproctis similis)*** and its hairy caterpillars are notorious for possessing poisonous hairs which cause severe irritation when handled. The caterpillars are common on hawthorn hedges in East Anglia and much of southern England. They are very conspicuous, having all the fiery brilliance of a red admiral butterfly, with their alternating stripes of scarlet, black and white, while the tufts of long grey hairs serve to emphasise their beauty as they sit on the green leaves in full view during the day.

Children are well advised not to touch them, since the loose poison-hairs quickly work their way into the tender skins of the young and produce a painful rash. There can be little doubt that the hairs are an effective protection against predation by birds, while the brilliant colouring gives adequate warning. When full-grown, the caterpillar spins a loose silken cocoon in which the threads are mixed with the hairs from its old skin, while the chrysalis also is hairy.

When the moth emerges, it collects poison-hairs from the cocoon and the old larval skin nearby, gathering them into the yellow fluff of its tail. The females do this very thoroughly and for a special purpose.

When the time comes for them to lay mat-like clusters of yellowish-brown eggs, which at first have a moist varnished surface, they deposit poison-hairs from their tails all over them. Thus, protective use is made of the hairs throughout life.

Male moths apparently ignore the reserve of weapons and make no attempt to gather the hairswhen they emerge. These males often fly to lights at night and they can be handled without risk. The caterpillars hatching from eggs laid in July or August usually hibernate while quite small and complete their growth in the following spring; but in some years when the moths mature extra early, there is a second brood of moths in September.

Pupa and caterpillars of the Yellow-tail
or Gold-tail Moth - *Euproctis similis*

A Fairy-Like Fly From Dragon Stock

Norfolk 3/7/54

In the stillness of a summer evening, when dancing gnats are beginning to dip low at the approach of dew and twilight, one may catch sight of a fairy like creature beating the air somewhat awkwardly with long gossamer wings as it makes a slow, rather helicopterous flight from one leafy bough to another. This insect is one of the green lacewing flies, a lovely creature with a delicate grass-green body and finely-netted, pearly wings. Its eyes flash forth a glow of fire and gold.

There is no mistaking it for any moth; not even the most weak-winged moth, apt to be whisked off its course by the least breeze, ascends with such frail grace and with so timid a launching into space. Its wings seem almost to blow away like folds of a diaphanous veil floating from the face of a bride upon a blissful morning.

For all its seeming innocence and gentleness, our lacewing comes of a dragon stock. Its immediate mission is to fasten small, white, pearly eggs on long stalks in such positions on the leaves of trees that when its infants come forth they will find ample provision in the way of greenfly.

The lacewing's children are miniature dragons, equipped with horrid jaws. They roam with stealth about the camps of the aphid hosts, devouring first the greenfly babies and later, when they are swaggering at the height of their powers, all-comers, young and old, winged and wingless, just as they happen to meet with them. The dragon grubs use the art of camouflage to perfection; not to increase their chances of taking helpless aphids by surprise – no such device is necessary – but to protect themselves from the unwelcome attentions of birds and other enemies.

They are adorned with innumerable little hooked bristles and bumps on the back, and skins of aphids and scraps of vegetable rubbish are fixed to the hooks so as to conceal the form and real colour of the insects.

One of the common green lacewing flies hibernates in houses and during its winter rest period it loses its green tint and becomes veined with pinkish brown; but when spring comes the green colour returns to its veins. There are also many brown lacewings especially associated with coniferous trees. One highly adventurous member of the tribe has forsaken the ways of its fellows and arranges for its grubs to feed on freshwater sponges in our rivers and broads.

Lace-Bugs With Exquisite Veined Wings

Norfolk 8/6/63

In tropical countries one meets with many large plant bugs of grotesque shapes, ornamented with leaf-like veins, false thorns, bark-like corrugations and filaments resembling strands of lichen, aerial roots, knobbly buds and so on.

In temperate regions bugs are mostly small and apt to be overlooked, but many are quaintly camouflaged in much the same way as their relatives living in equatorial jungles. We have Assassin bugs that look like short lengths of withered grass as they lurk in readiness to stab unwary insects; hawthorn bugs with thorns on their backs, red-brown bugs that mimic the bark of pine trees and thin green bugs that lie unseen on the leaves of sedges and turn straw coloured to match the colour of those leaves when they fade in autumn.

The lace bugs *(Tingidae)*, represented in this country by 23 species, might be considered the most elegant of all these insects. Not one is above a quarter of an inch long, and there is no vivid colouration, but their beauty lies in the exquisite lacy veining of the broad wings and rounded plates which fringe the foreparts of their bodies. There are also marble-like streaks and blotches of dark brown, grey and creamy tints forming attractive patterns on the lace, while in some cases a thin film of wax-dust produces a delicately sparkling "bloom" over the whole surface.

The rhododendron lace bug is the most conspicuous of its tribe. Actually it is an alien, thought to have been brought to England from America at the beginning of this century. It is a pest of many kinds of rhododendrons, mainly in our southern counties and some parts of East Anglia. If the boughs of infested bushes are shaken, thousands of these pale, glittering insects are disturbed. They fly only short distances, with jerky movements and soon settle on the underside of leaves and on the young shoots, where they suck the sap and make the foliage unsightly with brown stains. However, they seldom persist in one place for any length of time and appear to die out in cold winters so they are unlikely ever to be more than a minor pest in this country.

Two different lace bugs attack thistles and spear-thistles in our fields and in some years they play an important part in helping to eradicate these weeds. I have found up to two thousand on a single thistle. They look rather like lice and the attack is followed up by their dark, prickly or delicately spiny larvae. Some closely allied species have been distributed in Australia and elsewhere for the control of certain weeds, and their habit of breeding in large family swarms ensures that their plant victims are rendered impotent.

In the marshes of Broadland large beds of water forget-me-not are despoiled every summer by some very small, brown lace bugs, but the plants in this case usually prove too resilient, since they never lack moisture. They may be prevented from flowering, but new shoots come up later, when the bugs have wandered off to hide away in reedy litter for the winter.

"Teenage" Crows Enjoy Going in Gangs, Too

Norfolk 25/1/64

Of all the birds the carrion crow is the most detested by gamekeepers and country people who rear flocks of poultry, because it is the craftiest of egg thieves. Wild birds also suffer acutely from its depredations.

It is the habit of crows to perch like sentinels on the tops of isolated trees where they can see what is going on in all directions. When birds are building their nests their activities are observed and remembered by the watching crow, and in due course many nests are wrecked and robbed.

Later, when trees are more leafy and it becomes harder for the nests to be spotted, the crow is quick to observe other birds carrying food to their young and again he makes his merciless pounce when all has been discovered; this time he takes the chicks.

He may be considered a natural regulator of bird populations and to some extent he plays a useful part in improving the chances of birds which can manage to outwit him. For many years past I have lived in a marshy district inhabited by a good many crows, which nest unmolested in tall riverside trees. These birds take nearly all the first clutches of duck and waterhen eggs that are laid early in the season. In a cold spring, the chicks which would have hatched out from these eggs would in all probability die of starvation, whereas when further clutches are laid in replacement of those lost, the offspring stand a much better chance of survival.

If a bird loses its first eggs, it usually seeks a better concealed place in which to build its second nest and, in any case, there is always more natural cover from vegetation later in the spring. In learning to escape the vigilance of crows, birds also avoid the attention of some other predators, such as jays and magpies. They also tend to sit closely on their eggs and leave them, when they have to, with secrecy.

Outside the breeding season, crows often patrol the waterside, picking up carrion and attacking wounded birds in the shooting season. Some of them haunt beaches and estuaries where they eat shore-crabs and mussels, whose shells they crack by dropping them from a height. They tend to hunt in ones and twos, unlike rooks which go about in flocks; but I have seen as many as 40 carrion crows in a bunch in early summer. These were all young birds which had assembled from several nests, to travel round in a gang, as is the way of adolescents.

You may tell an adult crow from a rook by the black feathers covering the base of its bill where the rook has a patch of bare skin. The crow's caw is much more harsh and resonant than that of the rook.

In much of Ireland and Scotland, our carrion crow is replaced by the grey and black hooded crow; in the border zones, the two species interbreed. Why there should be two distinct races inhabiting adjoining climatic zones is a mystery.

Snow-White Buttonhole Flower

Fossditch at Weeting, Norfolk 25/2/61

Last week (February 25th) when I was in Breckland, I took a short walk along part of the ancient "Fossditch", at Weeting. I noticed masses of the bright green long-stalked leaves of the "button-hole flower", **Montia perfoliata**. It was covering much of the bank in the partial shade of a ragged belt of pines. In late April, there will be quantities of the small, snow-white flowers, bursting in sprays from cup-like leafy bracts. Nowadays, great sheets of these plants are a familiar sight in many parts of the Suffolk Breckland, usually where some trees are dotted about to give a little shade to the sandy soil.

There are similar colonies here and there in the Norfolk brecks and on hedge banks in many other parts of the county.

Yet when Nicholson's Flora of Norfolk was published in 1914, the plant was still a rare alien which had taken hold in only a few scattered localities. In the case of a good many foreign weeds, it has taken only a few years for them to become widely distributed and abundant all over Britain. The spread of the button-hole flower has been comparatively slow, probably because its seeds are heavy and shiny, so that they drop and slip into loose soil close to the parent plants.

This plant, rather oddly, comes from the Pacific side of North America, where it flourishes from British Columbia in the north to California in the south. The first known British-collected specimen was collected at Gorleston in 1837. How it arrived there is a mystery. Nothing more was heard of it in this country until 1852, when Octavius Corder (who later settled in Norfolk) discovered a flourishing colony at Amphill in Bedfordshire.A Norfolk botanist, Hampden Glasspole, rediscovered the Gorleston colony in 1859, and the plant is still growing there after a century, having spread gradually to several other spots in the "island" of Lothingland between Yarmouth and Lowestoft.

In Norfolk, Octavius Corder came upon a patch near a sand-pit at Rockland St Mary in the 1870s, and again the plant has kept going successfully in precisely the same place right up to the present moment. There has been a similar persistence in the Newmarket Road area of Norwich where seeds were introduced intentionally about 1880. Accidental introduction into the Suffolk Breckland appears to have taken place at about this time, but there was no spectacular spreading until afforestation began in the 1920s.

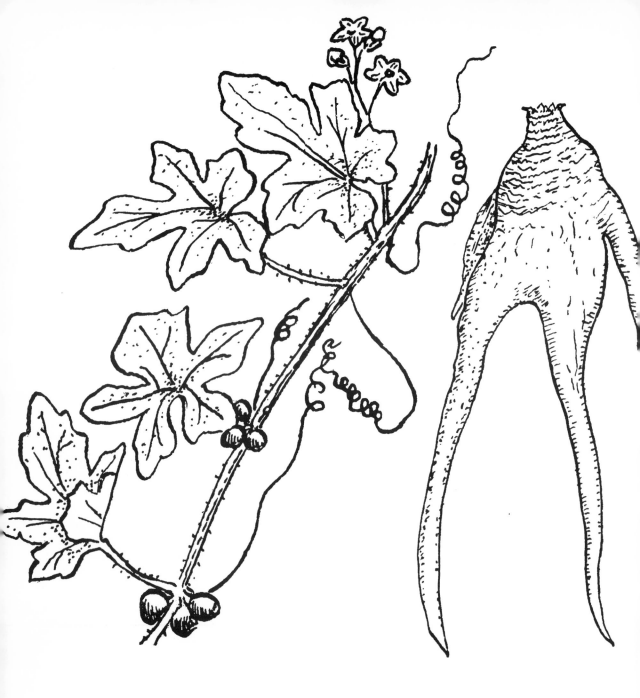

White bryony – known in this part of the country as Mandrakes. Animals tend to leave it alone because of its nauseous, irritant sap.

Plant Was Once Used in Surgery

Breckland 13/1/68

Many a time when I have been rambling across rabbit warrens in Breckland and elsewhere on East Anglia's lighter soils, I have caught sight of the massive, bleached, fang-like roots of white bryony exposed on the edge of a bank or mound. These roots become conspicuous when the sandy ground round them is loosened by burrowing animals and removed by rain and wind in the course of the years, while the plants continue to grow to a great age, with the tips of their roots still embedded below.

In this part of the country they are known as "Mandrakes" because, like the roots of genuine **Mandragora** which used to be imported by herbalists, they are often shaped vaguely like human bodies with trunk, legs and one or two arms, while their colour is that of creamy skin.

In the Middle Ages true mandrake was administered in wine, as an anaesthetic, to the victims of crude surgery. When patients were given too much, they never woke up, but at least some of them pulled round, if the dose was just right. Unfortunately, quacks sometimes used bryony roots as a substitute, with catastrophic results, since they are extremely poisonous, and this is why the plants are able to survive in country infested with rabbits or nibbled by sheep.

Bryony has a nauseous, irritant sap in all its parts, so browsing animals soon learn to leave it alone. The rather dull red berries can be eaten safely by birds but they are poisonous to mammals; the lethal intake is said to be 15 berries in the case of a child and about 40 for a man; luckily the fruits are not pleasant to taste, so, in practice, deaths from this cause are virtually unknown. I have been told that the dry, powdered root was given to bay horses to bring out their dark "hammer spot" markings in their summer coats.

White bryony, with its cucumber-like leaves and springy tendrils, is the only British representative of the gourd family. It flourishes, distributed by birds, in lowland England, but does not occur in Scotland or Ireland. The male and female flowers, with very rare exceptions, grow on separate plants and the "vines" die down and decay quickly as soon as the first frost comes in autumn. The plant's distribution pattern in this country seems to indicate that it likes a fairly dry climate; that of East Anglia suits it perfectly.

Poisonous Soap from Fragrant Flowers

East Anglia 21/9/68

The pink campion-like blossoms of soapwort (**Saponaria officinalis**) are an attractive feature of many a roadside bank at this time of the year

They have the bright texture and glossy foliage of the cultivated Phlox and their colour ranges from deep rose to the palest mauve or even white. In some colonies the flowers are single and are to be regarded as the representatives of the indigenous wild stock, but just as frequently they are double and larger, and these more ebullient flowers go by the name of "Bouncing Betty", which suits them very well.

Both varieties produce seeds, but rely on spreading by means of creeping underground shoots and the double form may be seen grown in cottage gardens here and there. By day the flowers are scentless, but they develop a delicious carnation-like fragrance at night and are said to have a very special attraction for hawk moths, whose long tongues are inserted deeply to reach their hidden nectar.

In East Anglia these plants are nearly always found near villages and the same holds good all over Britain except in the extreme south-west. Nowadays, it is rather difficult to define their natural distribution in Europe, because, although widespread, one is obliged to suspect that in many instances they owe their presence in the countryside to ancient cultivation.

In the Middle Ages and until fairly recently in some places cottagers were in the habit of using the leaves as a source of soap. They contain an appreciable quantity of saponin which can be extracted readily by bruising and steeping them in water. However, it has always been necessary to use the product with caution since the saponin is a poison when taken internally. It is this substance which renders horse-chestnuts unfit to eat, and it is found in the roots of wild arum which were once in great demand in this country as a source of starch.

Some centuries-old colonies of soapwort still survive here and there by Norfolk and Suffolk roadsides, and they often persist aggressively in the face of frequent mowing, mainly because they have very deeply entrenched rootstocks.

Soapwort - *Saponaria officinalis*

Celandine's Eye-Soothing Juice

Great Yarmouth 23/10/71

Greater Celandine (**Chelidonium majus**), with columbine-like foliage, yellow, four-petalled flowers and long, slender green seed pods is a common enough plant of garden corners and roadsides in most of our villages and it is to be found in similar situations pretty well all over Europe. Yet, it is not really a wild native of this country, but a relic of early cultivation. There is some evidence of its having been grown here by the Romans and it appears likely that they were responsible for its introduction as a useful herb. The ancient Greeks held its juice had the power of restoring the sight of blind swallows, which seems an extraordinary claim to us.

The plant has a bright orange-yellow sap which turns red on exposure to air. It has long been used as a country remedy for the cure of warts and corns, and I remember an old gipsy once telling me that it would "cure the yeller jarndice".

In the neighbourhood of Yarmouth and probably elsewhere, some cattle drovers used to soothe the inflamed eyes of bullocks with the juice of the herb when they were tormented with flies. (I came across the custom in the 1920s, but do not know if it persists.)

In ancient herbals chewing the root is recommended for soothing toothache, regardless of the poisonous purging effects of certain alkoids now known to be present in the sap. The juice is, indeed, very sharp and bitter to the taste, but like that of some poppies, to which the plant is closely related, it seems also to have opiate qualities. The foliage is avoided by farm livestock, probably because it has a deterrent odour. I have found that if the leaves are crushed in the hand and sniffed they cause sneezing.

When I gathered a few sprays for the purpose of illustrating this account, I discovered that the backs of the leaves were covered with tiny white flies similar to those which sometimes infest greenhouses; usually the plants are very free from insect damage.

This species is a perennial which bears flowers at intervals from spring to quite late in the autumn and may produce very large numbers of seeds in the season. The seeds are black, with shiny white appendages. They are commonly collected by garden ants which appreciate their rich oil content. The insects no doubt help in their dispersal.

Greater Celandine -
Chelidonium majus

Herb That "Soothed" before Aspirin

Norfolk 26/9/70

Feverfew (**Chrysanthemum parthenium**), with powerfully aromatic, lettuce green fern-like leaves and branching heads of small, daisy flowers, used to be grown very widely in cottage gardens. Nowadays it persists more by accident than design as a weed of walls, banks and town rubble.

I am just old enough to remember something of its fame as a "soothing" herb. Before the advent of aspirin, an infusion of its leaves or dried flowers was the most popular of sedatives taken for the banishment of headaches and the quelling of feverishness. It is, as its common name betokens, a genuine febrifuge, like its relative the camomile. Moreover, its strongly resinous odour and bitter taste may be said to have a peculiar attraction likely to take the mind off pain and melancholy when savoured in a medicinal drink.

However, as with so many herbal "remedies", there was no exact way of determining how much or how little should be imbibed to produce the required effect without also bringing complications of one kind or another and this is probably the main reason why modern drugs with their accurate criteria for prescription have swiftly outmoded the simples of the herbalist and the native medicines of the countryside.

All the same, the active principles of proven value in plants like feverfew are being analysed afresh in research institutions nowadays with a view to new forms of exploitation. In the case of this particular plant, for instance, the interest of a modern biochemist would certainly be aroused by the fact that feverfew had a reputation for arresting gangrene in the Middle Ages, when many people suffered from St Anthony's fire as a result of eating bread containing ergot of rye. Oddly enough, although the plant produces plenty of seed it never seems to become established as a field weed in this country.

The typical form is not thought attractive enough for cultivation in garden borders, but a yellow "button" variety is popular nowadays and has a very long flowering season. There is also a form with golden leaves used in formal "carpet" bedding.

A Nun's Herb for Childbirth and Hiccups

Carrow Abbey, Norwich 14/7/79

An ancient colony of Birthwort (**Aristolochia clematitis**) flourishes about the foundations of the ruin of Carrow Abbey.

A native of south-east Europe, this plant was widely introduced elsewhere as a medicinal herb in medieval times and in England, where it is comparatively rare, it is generally to be found associated with the ruins of monasteries and the like. Its presence at Carrow, although not actually recorded by botanists until 1793, suggests that it was almost certainly cultivated there by the nuns of that establishment which dates from the 12th century.

Its name indicates its most notable use as an aid in childbirth and although it must be classed as a poisonous plant, it has in the past been found valuable as an ingredient of ointments and poultices, while the powdered roots were used for cleaning the teeth and curing hiccups, according to a 16th century herbal in my possession.

The rootstocks are perennial and spread widely where the crumbling mortar of ruined buildings provides a sufficiency of lime in the soil in lieu of the limestone of the plant's native haunts.

The heart-shaped, quite smooth leaves have a rank odour which discourages browsing animals and may also be helpful in attracting certain small flies which play a special part in fertilising the flowers.

The slender, pale greenish-yellow, tubular, trumpet-shaped blossoms are peculiar in that the calyx forms the coloured portion instead of the corolla. As in the wild arum, small insects are trapped on entering the mouths which have downward-pointing hairs to prevent their escape until some time later, when the hairs wither and allow them to emerge, well dusted with pollen.

The projecting stigmas reach perfection before the stamens as each flower opens, whereby flies carrying pollen from older flowers effect fertilisation on arrival. Oddly enough, no store of nectar awaits the visitors, although one presumes that they must find some form of refreshment within.

The flowering season extends from June to September and under favourable circumstances spherical, striped capsules develop, packed with flat triangular seeds. The fruits hang downwards on curved stalks, ensuring that the seeds shall fall to the ground directly rather than relying on wind dispersal.

Decoy Flower Lures Insect Legions

Wheatfen 17/9/77

While some flowers are fashioned specially to attract only certain types of insect to help with pollination (examples include the snapdragon and foxglove visited effectively by bees) others make their nectar and pollen freely available to all comers.

The numerous umbelliferae with their multiplicity of small, usually white or pale yellow flowers grouped to form conspicuous, flat-topped heads are notable for their easily accessible nectar and on sunny days can often be seen crowded with insects of many different types.

In many cases, as is nicely demonstrated by hogweed, the outermost flowers of the umbels have larger petals than those in the centre, forming a lacy fringe which provides a finishing touch to the "advertisement", rather as the ray-florets of daisies help to emphasise the lure of the yellow "button" centres.

One very common umbellifer, the wild carrot, often resorts to a very peculiar little device apparently aimed at mustering the insect legions for a feast at its flower-tables.

In general, the massed blossoms are white; but commonly just one in the very centre is dark purple, appearing almost black; moreover, it stands slightly above the level of its fellows and assumes a somewhat crumpled shape, so that at first glance it looks remarkably like a dark-bodied fly. I believe that it acts as a decoy, just slightly tipping the balance in favour of those individuals which display it.

By no means all wild carrot flower heads possess this feature, so it is possible to compare those with and those without side by side as regards the numbers of insect visitors.

I once kept watch on two such umbels for half an hour on a sunny day, and found that nearly twice as many flies landed on the one displaying a decoy than on its neighbour which lacked the dark centre flower.

It has been found that carrots generally require to be pollinated by their neighbours with the help of insects, and, while it is clear that they are very successful in this and yield abundant seed under average circumstances, the use of the little decoy flower must be of some significance in the long term.

Plants With Novel Safety Device

March Railway Station 14/12/57

While I was waiting for a train on March railway station one morning recently, I happened to meet a botanist friend from Lowestoft and he told me of an interesting observation which he had made this autumn. He had taken a walk along the coast a few miles south of Lowestoft one day and come upon some sandy ground well spread with elegant rosettes of buck's-horn plantain. In the centre of nearly every crown of antler-like leaves spread over the sand was a hole, like a tunnel made by some burrowing insect.

Puzzled by the unusual appearance of the plants, he made a few careful excavations and discovered that what he had come upon was only an outstanding example of what is called root-pull. In other words, the plantains had drawn their crowns farther down into the sand at the approach of winter. The action must have taken place so swiftly that young leaves in the centres of the rosettes had not had time to develop so as to fill up the hollows.

Since my friend mentioned this, I have examined various other "rosette" plants and although I have not seen anything quite so spectacular as the sinking plantains, I have been able to detect examples of autumnal root-pull in the dove's foot cranesbill, field alkanet, viper's bugloss (in Breckland), cat's ear, dandelion, and the hoary plantain of chalk grassland. Most of such rosette-plants are biennials, which store their food in their roots at the end of their first season's growth and utilise it in producing flowers and seeds the following year.

The downward pull is achieved through the lateral swelling and vertical contraction of the root cells. In this way the plants become more firmly anchored in the soil before sending up tall flower stalks and at the same time their tender crowns are drawn a little way into the ground, where they are less exposed to the icy blasts of winter. Carrots are among these rosette plants and when they are harvested in autumn the wrinkles in their roots demonstrate the type of shrinkage which exerts the downward pull.

Anyone who has tried to dig up a snowdrop, crocus or bluebell must have been impressed by the depth reached by the bulb or corm in the soil. Under ordinary circumstances the seedlings of these plants begin life at the surface and each year they produce some special roots whose main function is to draw the bulbs farther down until they have reached the ideal level.

New crocus corms grow from the tops of the old ones, and without the aid of adjusting roots they would end up by trying to grow above-ground! The same applies to many other kinds of plants. Tussock sedges are an exception: they have no downward-pulling roots, so the tussocks grow higher until they topple over or die of drought.

Strawberry and bramble runners provide excellent examples of root-pull; even the connecting stems from the parent plants are often dragged underground.

The Mint With a Twist in It

South Wooton Norfolk 29/5/71

The oddest specimen reaching me by post this week was a strangely malformed sprig of common garden mint (**Mentha spicata**) sent by Mrs G Maclachlan, from South Wootton.

The whole of its stem was twisted into a neat spiral, with a broad "fan" of leaves sprouting from it on one side and spread out in one plane, each with a bud at its base. Such examples of this type of freakish development, known as spiral torsion, are rare but they have been recorded occasionally in a great variety of plants.

I have seen similarly twisted horsetails in my garden, a sweet william and a heat bedstraw in this condition, while very luxuriant asparagus often exhibits a certain amount of twirling in the strap-like fasciations which occur following a sudden check by frost. There is a remarkable kind of willow in which the trunk, stalks and leaves are all twisted, though not in tight curls.

Most plants twist about with a circular snaky motion as they are growing and this can be seen when the process is filmed and speeded up for demonstration. A gentle corkscrew pattern can be found in the bark of some common trees, such asthesweet chestnut, while a great many climbing plants twirl naturally and regularly in either right-handed or left-handed spirals.

Once in a while the habit of twisting becomes freakishly accentuated, and it is then that spiral torsion occurs. The cause is usually obscure and all one can say is that something goes wrong with the "mother" cell of a plant shoot at the critical initial stage of development. This may be due to some external stimulus, physical or chemical, or could arise by mutation.

In recent years the use of "hormone" weedkillers has resulted in the development of strikingly abnormal daffodils and other cultivated flowers and over-stimulated weeds tend to become strangely swollen and "strangled" in their death throes.

On one occasion when a cloudburst brought a spate of floodwater rushing through my garden from neighbouring farmland a number of yellow flag irises produced abnormal flowers for a season.

The soil is bedevilled with chemical residues very widely now, but fortunately most of the modern weedkillers have only a short life. However, spiral torsion in garden mint was noticed more than a century and a half ago by De Candolle in France, so it is no "new-fangled" kind of aberration.

Common garden mint (with a twist) - *Mentha spicata*

"Fairy" in the Garden Was a Leaf-cutter Bee

Wheatfen 21/5/60

One of my earliest memories of an exciting and mysterious happening in the garden where I played as a toddler comes back to me whenever I see leaf-cutter bees at work. I was about four years old, and we had just moved to a house which had been a monastery, with a great walled garden filled with all kinds of old-fashioned flowers and fruit trees. There were two moss roses, one white and one red, which had a great fascination for me, with their shaggy, sticky, balm-scented buds. Lingering on a sunlit path to stare at these bushes, I caught sight of a bright green leaf travelling through the air and flying in a straight line out of sight between some apple trees.

I thought I must have seen something in the nature of a fairy passing by. All agog, I kept watch along the path and eventually espied another green leaf dashing away; but this time it swerved and passed close to me, near enough for me to see that it was being carried by a sort of brown bee.

Soon after this, I found to my surprise that circular pieces had been cut from some of the rose leaves and later I watched two bees cutting segments of the leaves with their jaws snipping away like scissors, neatly and quickly.

A few years later, in another garden my father removed an unsound post with holes in it. He had split the post and tucked firmly into the holes I found two longish chains of little cigar-like packages made of faded green pieces of rose leaves. They had perfectly round leaf "stoppers" cemented on their ends. Breaking one open, I found it contained sticky and powdery material and a small white grub. Here was the answer to the puzzle of long before - these were the store-houses and cradles of the leaf-cutter bee.

There are several different leaf-cutters, all species of **Megachile**, in East Anglia. They have some resemblance to the honey-bee in size and colour, but are more hairy with larger heads to carry the massive cutting jaws. One species in particular snips rose leaves and, at times, petals. Another, found in dry sandy places, cuts out pieces from the yellow flowers of bird's-foot trefoil.

Elm and hazel leaves are attacked by a woodland leaf-cutter and one of the largest species, **Megachile maritima**, is not uncommon on our coasts, where it makes extensive raids on the foliage of privet bushes growing on the sandhills.

While these insects make good use of ready-made holes in wood for fashioning their cells, some excavate their own burrows in touchwood and in sandy banks. It happens frequently among bees and their allies, that the industrious and enterprising species attract lazy types which exploit their labours. The leaf-cutters are victimized in this way by Caeliozys bees, which steal a march on them while they are building their food cells by slipping in an egg while the leaf-gatherer is away for a few minutes.

Clump of Blue or Purple Hybrid Comfrey an Asset

Wheatfen 24/1/76

Although our native comfrey (**Symphytum officinale**) with winged stalks and either yellowish white or purplish flowers grows here and there in East Anglia's fensand river valleys, by far the commonest kind met with nowadays is the hybrid S. uplandicum, which often forms large patches by roadsides in relatively dry situations as well as on river banks.

This arose following the introduction of the blue-flowered "prickly" comfrey (**S. asperum**) early in the 19th century as a fodder plant. Crossing with the native species resulted in the production of plants showing various combinations of parental characters.

The flowers are usually bluish or heather-purple, but may be white, crimson or variously striped. Many are highly fertile, while others (those most nearly resembling the native species) are completely sterile so far as seed production is concerned.

Occasionally one comes across very vigorous specimens with large flowers which suggest polyploidy and some of these rampant forms are distributed as "Russian comfrey" for feeding to livestock and for the making of green manure. In some countries these hybrids are grown as a field crop with a high yield in silage. Then stocks are perennial and several cuttings of the leafy crowns can be made in a single season.

Comfrey roots are as black as liquorice on the outside, but white within and rich in mucilage. They have long been held in esteem for easing coughs and colds. In a 16th century herbal, the pounded roots are said to be "so glutinative" that when mixed with chopped or minced meat they "rejoine and bring it altogether again into one masse or lumpe". This gives a fair indication of the remarkable strength of the mucilage, which is comparable with that of arrowroot.

A clump or two of the blue or purple hybrid comfrey established in an old garden corner can be an asset in several ways. Leaves can be picked for feeding rabbits and poultry, the flowers are quiteattractive in late spring and summer and are much visited by bees and butterflies and the roots come in handy for medicinal purposes in winter.

Although the foliage dies down wih the coming of frosts in late autumn, new leaves develop rapidly when spring comes and shade out all competitors, including nettles. The plants seem to suffer hardly at all from the depredations of slugs and snails.

Busy Bumble Bees get the Blues

26/5/79

Bumble bees work very long hours taking little rest between dawn and dusk and braving the elements to a greater extent than any of our other flying insects. Their furry coats help to keep them dry and warm in wet and cold weather and the temperature of their bodies rises rapidly in flight, so increasing their sense of well-being as they buzz from flower to flower.

In early spring the queens emerge from winter quarters snugly underground, having mated in the previous autumn so that they are already in a state to raise their summer broods.

Presently, as more flowers become available to supply pollen and nectar, they select cavities, such as old mouse and mole runs as nesting sites, furnishing them with collections of dead grass, moss and leaves, in the centre of which they store a mixure of pollen and honey for their young.

Several eggs are then laid and these, with the food (bee-bread) are surrounded by a covering of wax to form a single brood cell. About three weeks later a posse of workers emerges to assist in food-gathering and the queen goes on to produce further broods throughout the summer, the nest being enlarged and furnished with special "honey pots" for the refreshment of all whenever needed.

Towards the end of the season, males and young queens are produced and by autumn the nests are deserted and only the new generation of queens remains to perpetuate the species in the following year, as happens with social wasps.

These bees play a very important part in pollinating a vast range of flowers. Their perception of colours extends to include ultra-violet radiation and many flowers emit signals at this end of the spectrum in addition to the colours seen by the human eye.

Bumble bees commonly take a great interest in the blue and violet flowers, being apt to investigate blue garments worn by walkers and a variety of objects displaying this colour. On fine days in the summer many of these bees can be seen flying straight out across the sea and it is common to find their drowned bodies washed up on beaches. Of the 18 kinds recorded in Norfolk, the white tailed bumble bee (Bombus lucorum) appears to be the most widespread and versatile in its range of habitats. One of the larger species, it is black, with yellow bands and a white tail segment. Although it has a short tongue unable to reach nectar in tubular flowers by way of the proper entrance, it takes a short cut to the sweets by biting holes in the flower bases when frustrated in this way. Present throughout Britain, its hardiness is shown by the fact that it flourishes in the sub-Arctic region of Europe.

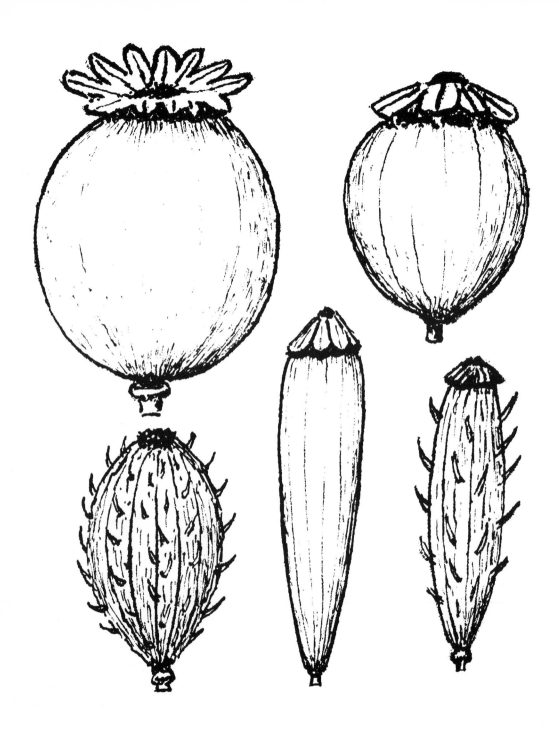

Poppy capsules – which contain seeds with the power to germinate even 60 to 80 years after being shed.

104

The Poppy's Soil Legacy

Norfolk 10/11/79

The vast and sudden burgeoning of poppies on the churned-up battle fields of Flanders some 60 years ago demonstrated the immense capacity of these weeds for springing up in profusion from long-buried seeds at the first opportunity. Without doubt, if one were to revisit those fields of blood today, green fields and orchards would be found obliterating the scars but, just as certainly, poppies are likely to appear whenever the soil is broken.

Seeds shed 60 or even 80 years ago retain their power to germinate when given a chance and since a single poppy plant may produce anything from 15 to 20,000 seeds in its urn-shaped capsules, the legacy left in the soil by even one summer's crop is vast indeed. It is small wonder that the corn poppy spread swiftly wherever the earliest tillers of the soil created settlements and there is evidence of the presence of poppies with the grain grown in England as early as the Bronze Age. In all likelihood, the original home of these plants was the Mediterranean region.

Several other kinds of poppy occur as weeds of fields and waste ground in this country, all of them hailing from warmer climes. The seed vessels of these species are distinctive. Next to the familiar scarlet corn poppy in abundance is the long-headed ***Papaver dubium***, with a long, smooth, slender capsule and brick-red petals. Another long-fruited kind, with sparsely prickly capsules is ***P. argemone***; it bears relatively small flowers with four rather narrow petals spreading in the form of a cross and orange in colour. It used to be quite common on sandy fields over much of Norfolk a hundred years ago, but now appears sporadically. The rarest of the tribe is ***P. hybridum***, distinguished by its brilliant crimson flowers and ovoid prickly capsules. It seems never to have been common with us and shows a preference for rather chalky soils; recent reports of its presence have come from the west of the county although I used to find it just south of Gorleston up to the 1930s.

None of these common species produces anything like the quantity of seeds yielded by the familiar ***P. rhoeas***; but this has a rival in this respect in the opium poppy (***P. somniferum***) whose very large smooth, spherical capsules are often dried for winter decoration.

This is a familiar plant in gardens nowadays, distinguished by its glaucous, quite smooth foliage and large, waxy blossoms. Garden forms of it have flowers of many colours, ranging through various shades of purple and red, both single and double.

This species is also grown as a field crop here occasionally for the oil in its seeds, while it is cultivated extensively in many parts of the world as a source of opium. Curiously enough, although grown in this country for at least 2000 years, it rarely appears as a field weed.

Persistent Field Poppy Seeds

2/7/77

The common field poppy (**Papaver rhoeas**) for which the cornfields of North Norfolk were once specially famous, contributes less of its flaring colour to our landscape than formerly, because of modern methods of control adopted on farmland.

However, it persists as a weed of freshly disturbed soil along roadsides and is quick to make a show on waste ground whenever it is given a chance. Its success is due to the capacity for lavish seed-production and to the ability of its seeds to remain viable for many years when buried in the soil.

Odd plants have a habit of appearing even in the midst of pastures where moles or rabbits break the surface and provide it with the opportunity to flourish on exposed earth, especially on light land. In this way fresh stocks of seed are added to the reserves, although their presence may remain hidden until the meadow comes to be ploughed some time later and an impressive crop of poppies appears.

It is virtually certain that the earliest cultivators of our soil brought the corn poppy to our shoreswiththeir seed corn from countries bordering the Mediterranean. There it is one of the opportunists, flourishing on the desert fringes when rain falls at irregular intervals.

Although the oily seeds can survive drought, the plants themselves are soon killed by frost and rely on making swift growth while summer sun provides energy.

The fertility of the flowers is assured through the production of innumerable stamens yielding pollen which attracts great numbers of bees and hoverflies. No nectar is secreted. Here and there one may come across a plant whose flowers produce their full quota of self-fertilised seed all the same. The flowers show some variation in colour, especially in the extent of the dark blotches of the petal bases. White and pink forms appear rather rarely in wild populations, but the famous Shirley poppies have been developed from these.

Some of the plants have yellow juice although this is normally white and some have hairs on their stems flattened instead of spreading. All poppies possess alkaloids, which are poisonous if eaten in sufficiently large quantities by animals, but the corn poppy does not yield opium. Nevertheless its juice has certain soothing properties.

Hover-Flies Foes of all Aphids

27/7/63

If you walk through a wood on a sultry summer day and look up into the treetops you will see hover-flies poised quite still in mid-air. From time to time they will shift their positions with sudden darts to one side, but in the flash of amoment they are still again with transparent wings holding them in perfect balance by a rapid fanning of the air. They disport themselves thus as a ritual preliminary to mating. In showing off, the males sometimes bump one another off course, and I have seen some giddy chasing at times.

There are many species of these flies, distinguished by the yellow, brown and black patterns on their flat bodies. In general, they assume the markings of wasps and bees and no doubt this mimicry often saves them from pursuit by birds, although there are birds which catch wasps and bees and likewise hover-flies.

They are of very great economic importance mainly because, like ladybirds, they are the foes of all kinds of aphids. They may be seen settling on the undersides of leaves where greenflies abound. The females go round sucking up the honey-dew and at the same time laying eggs at intervals. In a short time the eggs hatch and produce green, brown, grey or pink maggots. These hold on to the leaves by means of suckers and they wander round, using their foreparts like the trunks of elephants to lift aphids into the air and suck them dry. After feeding greedily in this way for a few weeks the maggots assume the chrysalis state stuck to leaves and twigs. In spring and summer they may run to several generations and, in a good year, they have multiplied vastly by the end of July.

Then it is not unusual for great swarms of them to migrate. They have been seen travelling steadily northwards along the East Anglian coast in hundreds of thousands on hot days in summer, and flocks of them have been met with far out to sea. No doubt a great many perish when these great dispersal movements take place, but it seems to be the inevitable result of overcrowding.

These insects also play a valuable part in helping to fertilise flowers. They eat pollen and drink nectar. If you watch a hover-fly on a flower you will see it using its proboscis like a vacuum cleaner, sucking up pollen dust from the anthers. It goes the round of the stamens doing this, then it dips low for a drink of nectar and by this means a certain amount of pollen is almost sure to be brushed off where the stigma is waiting to receive it.

Some of these insects are extremely hardy. Last winter (1963) after months of hard frost, I saw many hover-flies lurking unharmed in the buttons of Brussels sprouts, where they had been feeding on aphids.These were *Syrphus balteatus*, one of our commonest species and a regular migrant. Perhaps the most familiar of all these insects is the wasp-like *Syrphus ribesii*,it may be found in gardens everywhere and it is abundant in woods and along the hedgerows.

Harvest Field Gold

17/10/70

The pure, bright gold of corn marigolds (***Chrysanthemum segetum***) used to be a familiar sight in many a Norfolk harvest field. Indeed, on light, sandy grounds derived from ancient heaths and deficient in lime for that reason, the marigolds were much more in evidence than the poppies of "Poppyland" where the soil was not quite so poor.

In the Middle Ages this species flourished widely and was regarded as a very burdensome weed of cornfields, since it took so much out of the soil at the expense of the grain crops, more especially where there was little nutriment available in any case. It seems to have plagued our farmers from the earliest times and it was already well established at the Roman conquest.

Over the years it has acquired many provincial names, some indicating its yellow colour, such as "gule" (also a name for the yellow hammer), "yellow gull", "gil gowan", "guildweed" and "geal-seed", while another series of epithets clearly of different origin includes "boswell" "boodle" and "botherum".

It is an annual weed, some seeds germinating in autumn to stand the winter and others making a start in early spring. Flowering begins in June and continues until late autumn when the foliage is finally destroyed by frosts. The greatest display of blossoms comes from the stubbles after harvest and the waxy, blue-green leaves are efficient in conserving moisture, so that the plants do very well on relatively dry soil even when the rainfall is low in the late summer and autumn.

The flowers vary much in size, the largest being about two inches across. They are self fertilising, but are also visited by a variety of insects, including flies and butterflies. Seed production tends to be heavy in any case and while finches of various kinds devour a great many of the seeds, birds also help to disperse the seeds over the countryside.

At one time the leaves were used in pottage and salads by country folk and they also produce a strong yellow dye. In recent years corn marigolds have been largely eliminated from the fields, by the use of lime dressings as well as herbicides.

Long-Legged Harvestmen

Norfolk 23/10/54

As summer draws to an end and nights become cooler, it is common for some of the very long-legged spidery creatures known as harvestmen or harvest-spiders to find their way into our houses. At this time they are nearing the end of life and it is the warmth of our sheltering buildings that attracts them. They become adult in August and one then finds them resting on tree trunks and walls by day, while night finds them prowling over the ground and vegetation in search of dead insects and other waste materials in Nature's larder.

They are almost wholly scavengers and, unlike spiders, have no poison fangs for transfixing living prey. The very common species, ***Leiobunum rotundum,*** is gregarious in its habits when roosting, and I have seen as many as a hundred gathered on a south-facing wall of my house on occasion where an overhang provides cover from rain.

Some years ago, while inspecting one of these assemblies during the day, I noticed that the males, distinguished by their small round pinkish-brown "dumpling-like" bodies, had arranged themselves in a wide circle surrounding a dense cluster of larger females in the centre. At sunset there was a sudden stirring in the ranks. One by one, the females crept down the wall with males in close attendance.

From time to time they paused while mating took place and it became apparent that these ladies of the night were quite promiscuous, accepting as many as three husbands in succession before reaching the ground. Once these ceremonies were over, the harvestmen moved out in various directions to seek refreshment.

As weeks passed, the number of individuals returning to the roost became fewer and fewer. No doubt casualties accounted for this to a great extent, but in any case the impregnated females would have concentrated their efforts on depositing eggs in the soil and completing their mission in life and probably they would tend to roost in any handy niche once the urge to partake in the ritual of the communal roost was no longer a driving force.

By September it is clear that survivors of both sexes are simply prolonging their existence in a rather desultory fashion, sleeping rough and often lingering in tall vegetation where the fruits of autumn tempt them to live like lotus-eaters. They may often be seen imbibing the juices of over-ripe blackberries for instance. As might be expected, these creatures are very nimble and able to stride over obstacles at an impressive speed on their long legs whose terminal joints are highly flexible.

"Red-Leg" Thrives in the Rain

27/9/69

In autumn the flowers of pink persicaria or "red-leg" cover many stretches of low-lying arable land in Norfolk, providing a display of colour comparable with the scarlet of poppies in the north of the county years ago or the gold of corn marigolds on poor, acid stubbles.

This commonest of the willow-weeds is greatly encouraged by persistent rains, which enable it to develop over a much greater acreage than in normal seasons. It is also a species whose seeds are readily dispersed by water during winter floods; moreover, the seeds remain viable for close on half a century when lying dormant in the soil or in river mud. Sir Thomas Browne, in the 17th century, remarked on its appearance on mud thrown out of the ditches.

When lakes and broads are dredged, masses of persicaria flowers appear on the mud for a season then disappear as the result of other types of vegetation superseding them. When arable land is inundated for any length of time and remains water-slain until late in the spring it is sure to produce more persicaria than anything else in that year.

However, the plant is purely a summer annual and very often it disappears almost as fast as it comes, with some slight change in water level or cropping of the land.

Its seeds have been detected in quite ancient peats in this country, but it was probably somewhat rare until the first farmers began to till patches ofland along our river valleys, so providing the open conditions it required. When ponds dry up or are drained, it is often the most abundant plant springing from their beds in the first summer. It is very much a weed of the Fenlands, as one would expect. The seeds are devoured by many kinds of birds, including some wildfowl, and these help to introduce it to fresh places, while cattle also act as important agents in their dispersal.

Grazing animals avoid the foliage because it inflames the alimentary canal like cayenne pepper if consumed even in quite small quantities; therefore farmers regard it as poisonous to livestock. A common country name for it in Norfolk is smartarse and another is "Saucy Alice" and yet another was "Devil's Nip", from the dark "thumbmarks" on the leaves.

Pink persicaria - "red-leg"

110

Snow-White Moth that Resembles Heraldic Ermine

Norfolk 3/7/76

A great many moths are active at this time of the year (July) and, as dusk is merging into night, they can be seen rising from the undergrowth to flutter and dart erratically in all directions – some gently, like timid ghosts, others whirring and racing with the speed of arrows and, as often as not, circling at a height against the sky's afterglow, like ducks at evening flight.

When morning comes, most of them have vanished into secret hiding places where they will lie safe from hungry and inquisitive birds; but there are some which break this rule and sit boldly in the open when the countryside is flooded with sunshine.

One species often to be seen on dewy grass in the mornings now is the white ermine, a snow-white, softly furry insect whose folded wings are decorated wih small black spots so it resembles the traditional heraldic ermine. It is most usual to see two of these moths at rest near one another, one of each sex, which suggests that they have teamed up during the night, Their revelries are rather brief and soon the business of egg laying becomes pre-eminent.

In this species there is no difficulty about finding suitable fodder for the young, because most kinds of low-growing vegetation are acceptable to the caterpillars when they creep out of the egg shells in due course. They flourish best in deep cover, however, where marsh plants grow tall or weeds are rank on a waste patch.

Fifty years ago, when farm crops were commonly weedy, I remember seeing vast numbers of white ermine caterpillars devouring the commoner weeds. During harvest, swarms of these "woolly bears" were exposed in the stubbles and could be seen marching with undulating bodies in search of cover.

These caterpillars are dark brown, almost black, with numerous tufts of bristles and an orange-red stripe running along the centre of the back. They become full-grown in August or early September. In very hot weather, when the land becomes parched in some of their habitats, they have a habit of travelling in search of suitable cover for pupation.

At such times they may be seen crawling across roads in considerable numbers and I have known young cuckoos to gather in small flocks patrolling the byways, where they were finding and fattening on these caterpillars.

Halcyon Days of the Small Copper Butterfly

14/6/60

The Small Copper butterfly, with its fiery chequered wings, used to be one of the commonest insects on rough grassland, downs and dunes, appearing on the wing in every month from May to October. In the last twenty years it has vanished from many of its old haunts and one seldom meets with it in plenty. Its main strongholds left are along the coast, so far as East Anglia is concerned.

Why has it become comparatively scarce? The food plants of its pale-green, slug-shaped little caterpillars are the common and sheep's sorrels, both of which are still widespread in our countryside but not flourishing to anything like the extent they did in, say, the 1920s.

Nowadays common sorrel is eradicated from pastures by chemical spraying, while many thousands of acres of acid, sandy land which grew sheep's sorrel in the old days has been treated with lime and brought under cultivation in recent years.

The commons and dunes are by no means safe refuges either, because of the fires which sweep over them with dismal frequency whenever dry weather comes along. The halcyon days of butterflies are over in this country, at least for most of the grassland species. We shall never again see Small Coppers dashing about in hundreds over every meadow, as I remember them in the drought summer of 1921.

In that year there were four broods in succession and the butterflies behaved in an interesting way, producing many freakish varieties towards the end of the season. The early broods were the normal type, but by August a high proportion of the insects had crescents of bright blue spots within the copper bands of the hind wings. These spots were quite large in some instances. The squarish black spots on the copper forewings also became large and blurred in some of the later specimens.

In the late September and October a good many of the butterflies that I saw in the vicinity of Gorleston had light golden wings instead of the usual copper and a few were almost pure white in ground tint.

It may be that the summer's heat acting on the chrysalids played a significant part in producing these variations in colour. On the other hand, because the population of these butterflies was much larger than usual, there was an unrivalled opportunity for mutants to show themselves and for characters usually hidden to become revealed.

Now the chief reserves of these fiery insects in East Anglia is in Breckland, where sheep's sorrel abounds, and the use of agricultural poisons is not so great as elsewhere.

Painted Ladies Can Rest on Sea

East Anglia 8/9/62

During four days towards the end of June this year a migratory stream of Painted Lady butterflies, travelling northwards across the eastern parts of Suffolk and Norfolk, passed on towards some unknown destination, leaving only a few stragglers behind. Although it was not on a very grand scale, this passage of gay insects was spectacular for its suddenness and the people were quick to notice thebrisk flight of the strangers with orange, pink and chequered wings at the time when most butterflies were scarce.

For some years very few of these insects come to East Anglia but occasionally, as in 1947, they arrive in swarms and produce a late summer brood of caterpllars feeding on thistles.

Unlike the white butterflies which often arrive from across the North Sea, Painted Ladies usually travel from south to north, sometimes most thickly along the coast, but often moving in a broad band overland. Those that reach us in spring or early summer have flown from North Africa, crossing the Mediterranean and making their way to England in the course of a few weeks, if fine weather favours them. They travel against the wind as often as with it and are delayed only by cold or wet weather. Migration takes place mainly by day, but night flights far out at sea have been recorded.

Painted Ladies sometimes climb many thousands of feet to cross high mountain passes; at sea, they usually fly only a few feet above the water, and can rest on its surface and take wing again later unharmed. The migrants have been known to get caught in trade winds and forced to drift as much as a thousand miles from land in the Atlantic.

The Painted Lady of North America is the same species exactly as that found throughout Europe and Asia and, whereas our insects breed throughout the winter in desert margins of the Mediterranean and Red Sea, the American ones do so at that time in Mexico.

In each case there is a regular northward migration in spring. There is also plenty of evidence of a return movement southward, by the offspring of the spring travellers, in autumn.

Australia has a special race of the same butterfly, which sometimes migrates to New Zealand in the southern spring. On these rare occasions, flocks of Painted Ladies in numbers estimated to run into millions have been known to darken the sky like clouds of locusts, but such concentrations are unlikely ever to be seen by the time the insects reach England. They are apt to have become somewhat dispersed.

The last occasion on which anything like an immense swarm of Painted Ladies was seen in East Anglia appears to have been on September 20th, 1903, when thousands appeared suddenly from the west at Great Yarmouth, while the wind was blowing strongly against them. It seems probable that these butterflies were bound for sunnier lands.

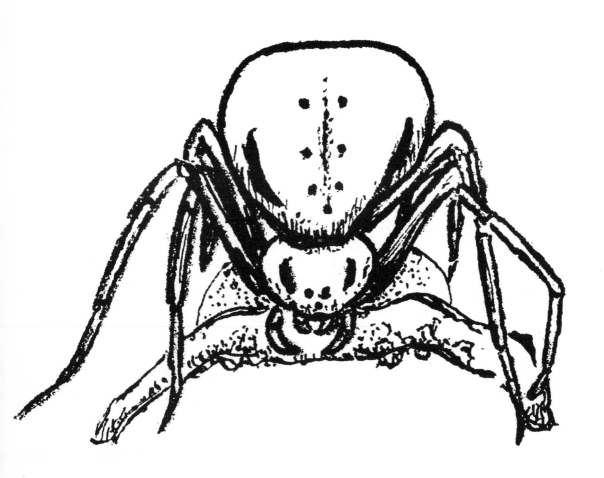

A deadly "kiss" – crab spider *Misumena vatia*, which can immobiliser much larger victims with its lethal bite.

Spider with the Kiss of Death

20/6/81

Most spiders go to the trouble of constructing snares for insect prey, but there are others which spin no such webs and merely leap on their victims suddenly or rush at them from secret hiding places.

One of the crab spiders, **Misumena vatia,** has developed the habit of sitting on flowers, with arms ever open to receive visitors, to whom she gives the kiss of death very promply with her poison fangs.

Like the similarly murderous praying mantis, she is well camouflaged so as to seem part of the flower chosen as the seat of her operations. The body and legs in most cases are white, often with a faint tinge of green, and these serve them perfectly when they squat on white flowers, as often happens. Like frogs and some fishes however, they are able to change colour to suit their surroundings. I have detected pink ones on the flowers of valerian and bistort and yellow ones lurking in the throats of yellow irises. In some parts of southern England the prevailing colour is yellow , to match the flowers of ragwort, broom and mullein.

In Norfolk, the umbels of hogweed seem to be the most popular perches of these assassins, which are mostly white, decorated with a few streaks of red and purple.

I have seen many different insects taken by them, including bumble bees, though more commonly various hover flies. However large and powerful the chosen victim, it is immobilised so swiftly with the spider's lethal bite that there is no struggle involved. After the victim's body fluids have been extracted, the spider just pushes its prey over the edge, leaving the way clear for the next victim to come along.

Only the females behave in this way; the males are much smaller and more conspicuously marked and may be found lurking in the shadows here and there. In some warmer parts of the world one meets with a number of other flower spiders indulging in the same habit of pouncing on unwary seekers of nectar. Some of these are specialists, mimicking their flowers very closely in form and ornamentation; but our native **Misumena**, through its chameleon-like ability to change colour, is able to operate from many different types of flower, changing its stand from month to month as the species succeed one another in their blossoming.

The spiders must have good eyes to guide them in their search for suitable perches. I have even found them seated on the umbels of giant hogweed 12 feet off the ground, involving a climb for them like Jack going up the beanstalk.

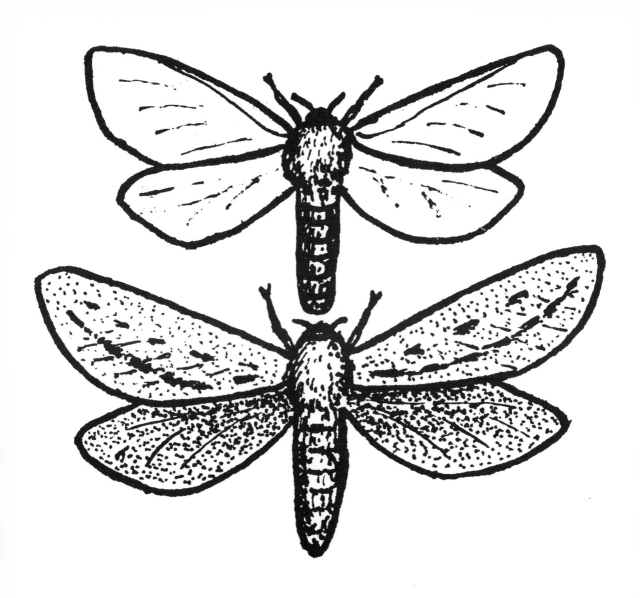

The Ghost Moth – *Heptalus humult* – which appears in June and July just at sundown.

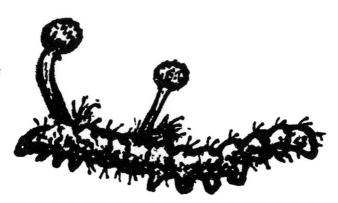

Ghost Moths

Blofield 10/3/84

Mr Harry Hammond of Blofield discovered some shining white grubs with reddish brown heads at the roots of potted chrysanthemums in his greenhouse recently (May '65). Similar subterranean caterpillars commonly appear in his garden soil and it would seem that the pot plants became infested when they were standing out of doors last summer. They were larvae of the Ghost Moth (***Hepialus humuli***) which feed on roots of many different plants, sometimes in such numbers as to do great damage to garden flowers and vegetables.

The moths appear in June and July just at sundown. The males, with a wing-span of about two inches, are pure white and display their charms to the larger yellow and grey females in a remarkable way, seeming to hang in the air a few feet above the ground swinging from side to side like a pendulum as though dangling from an invisible thread.

I have always assumed that they have come to be known as "ghost" moths simply because they are snow white and conspicuous in the glooming, but Mr Ken Durrant tells me he has witnessed mass flights of these insects in circumstances which have revealed that their performances have at times undoubtedly been mistaken for ghostly apparitions.

Some years ago, at North Elmham, he watched the dusk dance of a cloud of the moths and quite suddenly they vanished, dropping to the ground as a train made a noisy approach nearby. A villager who had been taking an interest in excavations taking place at the old priory there happened to be looking on and remarked that "the old grey lady's ghost" was still around.

On another occasion, Mr Durrant caused the shimmering white swarms of moths to vanish by clapping his hands.

Butterflies and the Deadly Drink

Buxton Heath 19/7/80

Many years ago, Professor F W Oliver came upon a large number of white butterflies trapped by sticky hairs of sundews on an island in one of the broads of the Ant.

I encountered hundreds of green-veined white butterflies which had met with a similar disaster in the boggy part of Buxton Heath, Hevingham, some time later.

In both cases it seems not unlikely that the butterflies were migrants; their presence in flocks suggests this, especially as the habitats of sundews do not provide food plants suitable for the caterpillars of these insects. The insectivorous sundews offer a lure to insects in the form of glittering droplets on the tips of their red hairs. So far as I have been able to detect, no scent is emitted as it is by most other plants whose flowers attract insects as pollinating agents.

Although butterflies commonly seek to refresh themselves with nectar, they also quench their thirst in other ways from time to time. In tropical countries vast numbers of gaily-coloured butterflies descend from the jungle to settle on the shores of rivers, lakes and estuaries where they imbibe moisture from the wet soil.

Some of our species display the same tendency on hot summer days. On various occasions, I have seen white butterflies, especially, congregating on wet sand and rocks by the sea to drink salt water. At other times, I have noticed them taking moisture from liquid manure in farm yards and from a wet path strewn with ashes alongside a dyke in my garden. They may also settle on the "beaches" of freshwater reservoirs to quench their thirst without risk of drowning - which might be involved were they to attempt direct contact with open stretches of water.

In this country the butterflies behaving in this way seem to be chiefly the small and green-veined whites, but I have also seen Red Admirals, Greylings, Small Coppers and Holly Blues drinking from moist ground.

However, sundews are clearly most likely to make a spectacular catch when flocks of white butterflies are migrating overland in the heat of the summer and glimpse sparkling refreshment in boggy places.

The deadly drink - trapped by the sundew

A Moth of the Darkness

Wheatfen 7/8/71

On opening a cupboard, or even lifting the bonnet of a car on occasion, I have often been startled by the emergence of a large sooty moth, known as the Old Lady, well named for its dress of funereal satin with lacy ornamentation. Appearing about the end of July, it flies by night and is attracted by sap oozing from wounded trees but, as dawn approaches, it dives into hiding places and remains hidden until well after sunset.

One day I discovered three of these moths roosting under a wooden lavatory cover. They vanished when night fell, but were back in their former positions next day. On the following night I kept watch and saw one of them scuttle away to reach the open air by a devious route.

This departure and return continued for a week, establishing the fact that the insects "homed" to their lodgings with remarkable precision, a habit not known previously in moths. Another instance of this behaviour was recorded in another Norfolk locality in the summer.

I once flushed one of these moths from under the hood of a child's pram. This made me wonder if the horror of moths evinced by some women may have arisen from the experience of nurse-maids long ago when tending their young charges. I have heard the name "Padge" applied to these witchy insects of darkness. This name is shared by the Barn Owl in some parts of England.

Funereal - the Old Lady Moth

119

Minute Mites with Many Parts to Play

26/11/77

Mites, which are diminutive relatives of spiders, make up for in numbers what they lack in size and play many parts in the economy of nature, several types abounding in the soil and others feeding on leaf-litter and fungi.

We have hairy cheese-mites, flour-mites and house-mites. Various "red-spider" mites, some being spinners of silk, suck the green life from plants and there are numerous species which produce galls and in some cases become vectors of viruses affecting plants and animals.

Blood-sucking red mites attack fowls on their perches at night; feather-mites live in birds' plummage and many are responsible for diseases such as mange and sheep-scab. Harvest-mites, when young, burrow into people's skins and produce "heat bumps", but later lead an innocuous existence out of doors.

Honey bees are sometimes suffocated by parasitic mites which clog their breathing passages (Isle of Wight disease). The velvety, scarlet mites often to be seen crawling over mossy soil spend only part of their lives as parasites plaguing grasshoppers.

Similarly, many of the elegant water-mites of our ponds and ditches attach themselves to aquatic insects, including water scorpions, pond skaters, dragonflies and gnats and take nourishment from these hosts when young, but not when they become adult.

It is common to find golden-brown mites clustered on the bodies of bumble bees, carrion-beetles and dung-beetles; but these are only scavengers hitch hiking on their hosts as a means of dispersal; they specialise in cleaning up waste matter in underground nests. Once a friend sent me minute orange-red mites infesting a small mottled willow moth taken in a light trap at Cley. These proved to be ***Cheletomorpha lepidopterorum***, typically, though by no means commonly, parasitic on certain moths.

As can be seen in the illustration, this species is equipped with workman-like pincers which presumably assist in dealing with the scales covering the bodies of the hosts.

Moths resting and immobile during the daylight hours are most probably open to infestation when they frequent farm premises where the mites lurk in such places as cattle feed bins and barn floors. In this instance the parasitised moth was one famed as a sporadic migrant and sometimes, in its caterpillar state, a pest of beet and potatoes.

Oil Beetle Grub Has Only Slimmest Chance of Survival

17/3/73

When I was a youngster, oil beetles were a familiar sight on the grassy banks when the first days of spring came along each year. I do not often meet with them nowadays, so perhaps they have become victims of pollution along the roadsides. They are large, blue-black and torpedo-shaped and look awkward, trundling their clumsy, egg-stuffed bodies behind them. They pause to nibble green stuff here and there and I have seen them feeding on freshly opened flowers of dandelions. They expose themselves quite freely and rely on an oily, acrid fluid which is emitted immediately they are handled.

At intervals these beetles deposit clusters of minute yellow eggs, thousands in each batch, an inch or so beneath the surface of the soil. The larvae which emerge from these eggs a few weeks later are very lively little creatures which look like bird lice.

They swarm on to the tops of flowers and attach themselves to the legs of bees and other insect visitors. Most of them go astray, but those that happen to cling to the right kind of solitary bee stand a chance of survival. On arrival at the bee's nest-cell, the larva must eat the egg of its host and then undergo a physical change which allows it to feed and grow like a bee grub. The chances of success are very small and this is why the beetles lay such great numbers of eggs.

A greatly magnified louse-like "triungulin" larva is shown next to a normal-sized beetle in the illustration.

Some of the oil beetles in various parts of the world parasitise grasshoppers and locusts, the so-called "spanish fly", a metallic green beetle (***Lytta vesicatoria***) is reared by bees. It visits Norfolk as a migrant once in while but does not seem able to persist for any length of time.

Another beetle in the same family breeds only in underground nests of the common wasp; it is seldom met with in the open, but may be looked for with a greater chance of success in the contents of a nest which has been killed off and dug out at the end of the summer.

This Beetle Lives up to its Name

Breckland 9/5/54

Dragonflies are aptly named and must strike terror into the consciousness of their insect prey; but compared with tiger beetles they are frail, waggly-headed creatures, easily dinted and daunted and altogether archaic with their enormous eyes and mincing mouths.

Tiger beetles are mostly winged devils of the Tropics, where they dart with lightning speed from rocks and sand burned by the sun or launch themselves from scorched savannah trees to seize and dismember other winged minions of the air.

In England, they stand out from all other insects as the fiercest and most dashing of brigands. In our East Anglian breck country and on patches of sandy heathland here and there one sees them scuttling over hot, bare places in spring and summer or flashing in golden flight above the heather. Their wing-cases are usually of a vivid and poisonous green, like the rock malachite, and spotted with white devil-eye markings. Breckland specimens are sometimes bronze-tinted (in life) and the green colour is replaced by black occasionally.

Tiger beetles have noticeably projecting eyes which can see all round, and their toothed jaws are very formidable, being specially hard and strong and sickle-shaped. They attack their prey with a rush and make mincemeat of their victim in no time. When two tiger beetles are confined together they are apt to become engaged in mortal combat and sooner or later one is bound to be torn to pieces, or rather, be dismembered as though by a guillotine.

Even in childhood, these creatures have a tiger-like ferocity. As larvae, they live in vertical tunnels in the earth. The shafts are anything up to a foot deep and the tiger grubs lurk at the entrances with eyes on the alert and scissor jaws ever ready to snap at any insect coming within range of a quick leap.

When the prey has been seized it is at once dragged to the bottom of the pit and devoured at leisure, there is no escape from such a dungeon. I have seen the earth honeycombed with tiger pits, and have teased the fierce inmates by tempting them to snap at thistle down; but they soon discovered their mistake and ejected the unrewarding prey from their burrows.

Tiger beetles are among the very few British insects capable of wounding the hand, but so far as I know their bites are not poisonous; they are strong enough to deal with their prey without resort to poison. Some tiger beetles are said to emit averbena-like scent when handled. I have not noticed this in the common green species found in this part of the country.

When Billy-Wixes Crowd

Gorleston 20/8/83

Summer cockchafers (***Amphimallon solstitialis***) sometimes appear in large numbers from the end of June to early August, chiefly in coastal areas, but also inland where the sandy turf of lawns and golf courses provides suitable habitats for their grubs.

Known variously as "Blind Bees", "Midsummer Dors" and "Billy-Wixes" (this last name being shared with the Barn Owl), these beetles emerge from the ground round about sunset, buzzing around tall objects such as trees, chimney-stacks and even bushes on open ground.

They even bump into people walking on summer evenings and can be a cause of some consternation, especially when they tumble down chimneys into bedrooms and make clumsy attempts to escape from windows, although they are not in any way dangerous.

About three quarters of an inch long and of a light reddish-brown colour, they are "hard-shelled" and hairy, with horny, curving, clawed legs and antennae tipped with antler-like lobes.

Their evening assemblies are chiefly for nuptial purposes, like the swarmings of gnats; but the beetles also alight on treetops and make a supper of juicy foliage, causing heavy defoliation at times. They are not without enemies when they throng the air. I once saw many noctule bats catching them round the tops of poplars near Gorleston as a golden afterglow in the western sky silhouetted the scene of activity. I could hear the snapping and crackling as the bats seized and crunched their bodies.

Although clumsy in their movements, the chafers are not blind but, as in other insects swarming for mating purposes, the habit of massing darkly over tall objects has the advantage of drawing the attention of stragglers to the festive party.

The mating ceremony over, the females seek dewy turf and insert their eggs at the grass roots. In due course the half-curled, whitish grubs grow to maturity over a period of two or more years.

Major emergences of the chafers occur with some irregularity. The summer of 1983 has been marked by their abundance, whereas they were relatively scarce in the wet summer of the previous year.

Sandy ground suits them best, as the beetles encounter no difficulty in breaking the surface, both when emerging and when egg-laying, whereas hard-baked clayey soil poses problems.

Summer cockchafer -
*Amphimallon
solstitialis*

123

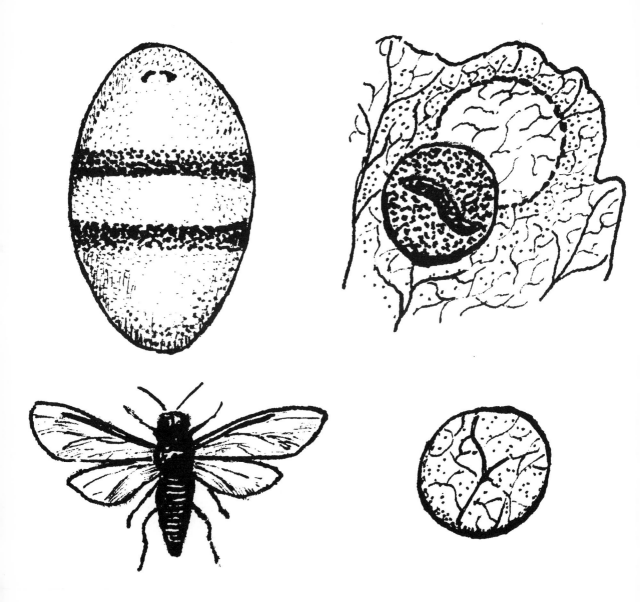

Jumping bean? It's the cocoon containing the larva of a sawfly which is able to make the container bounce by undertaking violent contortions.

"Jumping Jack" Propelled by Caterpillar

8/7/72

Once I came upon what looked like a miniature "Humpty Dumpty" hopping about on our gravel drive.Shaped like a hen's egg, but only five millimeters in length, it was in fact a horny, reddish-brown cocoon with a light grey belt, edged blackish, round its middle.

When I first noticed it, it was leaping about like a "jumping bean" in bright sunshine, each hop carrying it on anything up to two inches. Later, when it was placed in a glass jar, we found that whenever it was exposed to a fairly strong light it soon started skipping again and on one occasion, when sunlight streamed in through a window to illuminate it continuously, it remained lively for two hours at a stretch without appearing to tire of its gymnastics.

The cocoon contains the larva of a sawfly which, by making use of a silken spring-board and the elasticity of the central belt region of its "shell" contrives to tip and bounce the container at will when it undertakes violent contortions.

I know of only one other insect which behaves in this way in this country. It is the "jerking disc" sawfly whose larvae inhabit blotch-mines in sycamore leaves eating the sappy green cells between the upper and lower surfaces.

When a larva is full-fed it makes a series of little perforations like those on a sheet of stamps, but in a circular band, cutting only the upper skin of the leaf. It then spins a sheet of silk as an undercoat, sealing the rim and finally detaching its "case" so that it falls to the ground.

Then, by using its cushion of silk as a springboard, it is able to travel by a series of jerks until it has found a suitably shady spot in which to rest secure during the ensuing winter. It retains itsmobility until the following spring, when pupation takes place within the cocoon and the adult sawfly emerges in due course.

The "jumping beans" imported alive as novelties from Mexico are the seeds of a spurge containing larvae of a moth closely related to the codlin moth which infests apples. They react to heat by leaping and in nature this is their way of escaping a scorching from the sun in the "dry" season.

These grubs also use little pads of silk for generating their sudden hops, using what amounts to a catapult action in which they themselves are the missiles striking the walls of their chambers so sharply as to make them bounce.

Leaves Take Nourishment from Insects

11/11/66

When leaves assume the fiery tints of sunset and fall from deciduous trees in autumn, most of them soon wither to some shade of brown in dank carpets underfoot. Here and there, however, some of them retain little patches of vivid green, like islands of verdure enclosed by veins and these may persist for several months despite the fact that the leaves have no connection with their old life-stream of sap which fed them when they were attached to twigs.

If one looks closely at the leaves with green blotches it becomes evident that in most instances they are disfigured in some way as the result of attacks by leaf-mining insects.

Such insects, which comprise the larvae of many very small kinds of moths and flies, tunnel under the skins of the leaves and devour the green cells. Some of them produce blisters and others construct elegant winding galleries which may be serpentine in form or coiled like the shells of snails.

Green patches may also be found associated with protuberant galls occupied by the larvae of midges or gall-wasps and from time to time I have found them where leaves have been attacked by certain parasitic fungi or merely soiled by bird droppings.

What appears to happen in all these cases is part of the leaves are able to remain alive because they are nourished by chemical substances stemming from their despoilers. In other words, they make use of nitrogenous waste excreted by the leaf-miners in their tunnels, gall-insects in their vegetable huts and fungi through their myselial strands (by osmotic exchange), while in the case of bird droppings the external application of manurial stimulants is accidental.

Nowadays, nutrients are sometimes sprayed on the leaves of orchard trees to improve their productivity and it is interesting to find that the principle involved is one of nature's own. Moreover, the green islands persisting on dead leaves demonstrate the "give and take" arrangement by which many small animals and plants manage to live together harmoniously under natural conditions.

Insect Musicians of the Autumn Evenings

Norfolk 22/9/56

The autumn dusk is often filled with the jinking music of insect nightingales for those who walk the lanes or take the evening air in country gardens. The little instrumentalists perform with cymbals and remain anonymous to most of those who listen to their triple chirrups, silvery and staccato, just above the whisper of leaves. These ventriloquists of the shadows are plump, brown, wingless grasshoppers, sometimes called "bush-cheeps", (***Pholidoptera griseoaptera***). Although they shun daylight in the autumn of their lives, they have known the pleasure of basking on sun-warmed leaves when they were striped and freckled, spidery infants practising their climbing powers among the nettles and brambles.

I have often meant to keep in touch with these creatures regularly for a whole summer season; But somehow they always elude me between June and the middle of August, when the chirruping begins. They are well camouflaged in streaked and speckled brown, of course, but one would think that they might be discovered at the parting of branches or in the prodding of lower vegetation occasionally; yet they slip out of ken completely for a good two months while they are waxing big.

I have seen the babies drinking nectar on umbelliferous flowers and devouring aphids in May and have surprised adultsin the act of eating snails and caterpillars on wet overcast days in autumn.

It is held by entomologists that bush-creeps are in general carnivorous; but very few observations of their feeding habits have been made. Like some of the green tree grasshoppers, they have occasionally been found imbibing the treacle bait smeared on tree trunks by moth-hunters. It is possible that they may be among the insects to tap the juices of the mysterious leaf-nectaries developed on various trees and shrubs.

This week, (22/9/56), I have listened to the bush-cheep chorus in the misty moonlight on two evenings when the air has been perfectly still. I have heard differences in the speed and pitch of thestridulations and have noticed the closer and closer approach of insects calling and answering one another. Do rivals clash and fight to death? Do the females devour their husbands? We just do not know the answers to these questions; they are still secrets of the dusk.

Bush-cheeps are both fierce and strong and it is conceivable that they resort to partial cannibalism, like some other long-horned grasshoppers. Their hearing organs are not in their heads, but in little slits in their front legs. They lift and move these legs about when gauging the position of a rival songster.

The males vanish first from the scene as the nights get colder and by the end of October the lingering females have plunged their sword-like ovipositors into the damp earth and laid clusters of eggs secure in gummy cases to withstand the perils of winter.

Snow fleas - link with Ancient Life

Costessey 8/3/80

In my lifetime there have been discoveries of "living fossils" which have thrilled the scientific world. The coelacanth representing a type of fish thought to have been extinct for 40 million years turned up off the African coast in 1938 and a similar primitive conifer, the dawn redwood was discovered in China in 1941.

The sensation made by such finds, however, tends to obscure the fact that many plants in our midst are equally archaic and have undergone little change in their forms and habits since they first appeared on earth many millions of years ago.

Among plants, the horsetails are a good example, while the dragonflies flying over our ponds and rivers are little different from their ancestors which inhabited primeval swamps in the coal age.

Some of the more primeval types of insects have a few modern representatives and this applies in our countryside to the very ancient scorpion-flies, two kinds of which, equipped with two pairs of long, transparent, spotted wings, can be seen flitting clumsily and resting on plants in summer. The male is characterised by orange-red, up-turned, scorpion-like tails.

We also have another, much smaller member of the family which is active in winter. This is the Snow Flea, **_Boreus hyemalis_**, so called because it can sometimes be seen skipping about over snow in a jerky, flea-like manner. Scarcely three millimetres long, this lively brown insect has only slight vestiges of wings, reduced to tiny scales in the female and curved bristles in the male.

Like its larger relatives, it is distinguished by the possession of a long, beak-like "face" with jaws at the tip. It feeds on mosses, just as its ancestors may be expected to have done 250 million years ago, when no flowering plants as we know them had yet appeared on earth.

Their larvae also feed on mosses, pupating in the soil and emerging as adults in October, to continue in this state throughout the winter. Snow fleas were first noticed at Costessey by Dr W E Leach early in the 19th century, when the pioneers of local entomology, centred on Norwich, were very busy in the neighbourhood.

Since then, strangely enough, these insects have been generally overlooked while enthusiasts have concentrated attention on butterflies, moths, beetles and bugs.

A few years ago, however, Dr Eric Duffey came upon them in great abundance on one of the Breckland heaths and it is possible that, if properly searched for, they would prove by no means uncommon in this country.

Cricket Chorus in Every Hushed Street

14/1/61

Shortly after the wartime "black out" had been introduced, in the autumn of 1939, I had occasion to walk from Old Lakenham to Upper Hellesdon going through the middle of Norwich, one rather mild night.

There was little or no traffic and I met scarcely a soul in the streets. The city seemed to be dead, so great a hush had fallen upon it. It was in these strange circumstances that I enjoyed an experience unlikely ever to be repeated.

From the moment I set out, to the journey's end, the shrill staccato chirpings of house crickets assailed my ears. The insects chanted in every street and after a mile or two of their company I came almost to believe that the high-pitched creaks pricking the night came from hundreds of tiny missiles whistling their way down from the stars.

The bombardment reached its greatest intensity, I remember, as I turned out of Duke Street towards St. Augustine's. Norwich used to be plagued with crickets, especially after warm summers. But modern insecticides have made a big difference and nowadays, householders' complaints of infestation come mainly from suburbs abutting on refuse tips. This is because the insects find conditions very favourable for breeding in masses of garbage and damp waste paper, which generate heat almost to the point of spontaneous combustion in the dumps, even in winter. Adult crickets take wing at dusk in large numbers over the rubbish-tips and attract many bats, while even owls come to take part in the feast.

Some of the insects go off and enter houses, especially in the autumn, and in due course take up their traditional stations on or close to the hearth, or the kitchen stove. In early Victorian days they swarmed especially in bakers' offices, where they were assured of a good heat perpetually.

It is not known how long house crickets have been in this country, but they are believed to have originated in North Africa and to have found their way here in ships long ago. Given enough warmth they breed all the year round and their chirping is a song of challenge and courtship rather than an expression of idle merriment. Crickets have "ears" in their front legs by the way.

The body of the house cricket is yellowish brown, with darker mottlings. This distinguishes it at once from the slightly larger field-cricket, which has a shiny, almost black body marked with a yellow band in front.

Titbits for Friendly Slugs

Wheatfen 7/11/64

Friends who come to stay in my house are always asked to avoid treading on the slugs which glide over the polished floors of the hall and one of the downstairs rooms at night.

Usually, these creatures emerge from behind the skirting boards only after the household has retired to bed and they have slipped into hiding again by the time we are abroad in the morning, so that on the whole they run little risk of being walked on.

If we come home late from a party however, we find them in the midst of their nocturnal revels, roaming in search of odd crumbs and other fragments of edible garbage which may have reached the floor during the day. Sometimes, on such occasions, we treat them to a little cake, bread or cheese, because they probably have a rather thin time of it during the greater part of their existence.

Our favoured lodgers are yellow house slugs *(Limax flavus)*, which are rarely to be found away from houses and outbuildings. It may be that long ago they struck up a close association with our ancestors who lived in caves and provided quantities of garbage. Later, the slugs continued their commensal way of life in mud huts, buildings of wattle-and-daub, stone and eventually brick. In parts of Europe where the climate is mild and damp they can be found living away from human habitations; but in the north they are confined to houses.

The usual colour is clear yellow with translucent grey marblings, but there are also red, grey and black-spotted orange varieties. When young, they are often greenish and sometimes brown. Full-grown specimens a year old reach a length of four inches and look quite beautiful by lamplight, since they have the transparency of amber. The eggs are laid in chains under rotten boards and the like, at intervals throughout the summer and autumn, and slugs of all ages and sizes are present throughout the year.

Self-respecting housewives are unlikely to tolerate slugs indoors when they find tell-tale slime trails on floors and carpets, and the hygienic conditions found in modern dwellings tend to exclude these fellow-travellers from the past; but no doubt they will linger on for many years yet in old country cottages and farm houses.

As scavengers, they have their uses. They have a taste for dry rot fungus, for instance, and they are quick to consume the remains of such things as dead mice under the floor-boards, as I know from experience in my own home

Pub Spiders Travel with the Beer

3/4/71

The "Daddy-long-legs" spider, **Pholcus phalangioides**, resembles some of the common "harvestmen" in possessing extremely long legs.

It flourishes greatly in houses along the south coast of England, festooning ceilings with extensive webs which, though so delicate as to be almost invisible in themselves, soon become conspicuous when coated with dust and converted into vast, ragged cobwebs. The body of this species is cylindrical and of a light yellowish-brown colour, with a few dark patches on the abdomen. The female is larger than the male and lives longer, but even she is quite small, with a body-length of 8mm. She carries her eggs around.

Her web covers a large area like a rather loose net and when insects or wandering spiders of other species fall foul of it and begin to struggle, the owner causes the web to vibrate by jerking her body up and down with a sort of twist. One could almost describe her motion as "whirring", since it is so rapid that the spider's shape is blurred like the sails of a windmill on a breezy day.

Large and unwieldly intruders are alarmed by this and tend to break free (they would only be a nuisance) while smaller prey tend to become embarrassed and more entangled by the threads.

Away from the extreme south of the country **Pholcus** is a rare spider, limited by its aversion to low temperatures. When Dr W S Bristowe was mapping the distribution of British spiders some years ago, he was able to find this species surviving away from its native area only in cellars with an equable temperature in the low fifties F.

In 1961, I was much surprised to discover a number of these delicate house-spiders on the ceiling of the main bar at Coldham Hall by the riverside at Surlingham. Soon afterwards the room was redecorated and I saw nothing more of the spiders and with the intervention of an arctic winter in 1963 it seemed unlikely that **Pholcus** would reappear.

However, some survived and an extensive pub-crawl might well reveal the presence of **Pholcus** at many other local inns. It is quite possible that such spiders are commonly delivered from the brewers' stores with crates of bottled beers, just as French cellar-spiders have been known to arrive in this country with well-matured wines.

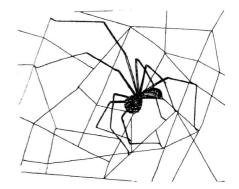

Daddy-long-legs spider -
Pholcus phalangioides

131

Cave Spiders Lurk in East Anglia

Norwich 12/12/82

The engineers who help to maintain our telephone service are often required to attend to junction boxes housed underground in various parts of the countryside.

In the course of their work, they are apt to encounter strange "beasties" on lifting manhole covers and probing the cavities in which vital apparatus is requiring adjustment.

The team operating from the Norwich telecommunications centre has drawn my attention to some large colonies of dark, long-legged spiders inhabiting some of these recesses, especially in North Norfolk.

These are cave spiders, mostly of the species ***Meta menardi,*** which spend their lives in the darkness of dank natural caves or, in substitution, cellars, tunnels and culverts all over the British Isles nowadays.

They are fairly large, with dark brown or almost black, shining bodies about 13 mm long and long legs which are cross-banded and somewhat spiny. Their prey consists largely of woodlice and, like other spiders which feed on these armour-plated crustaceans, they are equipped with strong, sharp fangs. However, I have not come across any evidence that they are capable of piercing the human skin and inflicting even mildly poisonous bites.

Hanging within the dark cavities from time to time one can see their white egg cocoons hanging like silken bladders. Swarms of young emerge from the eggs in due course and presumably feed for a while on some of the other small inhabitants of underground lairs, such as springtails, mites and perhaps some of their own brethren (as happens with the young of garden spiders living out of doors).

Early in 1981, my Telecom friends unearthed one very black and shiny female cave spider from a manhole at Henham and this when examined by Dr. Anthony Irwin at Norwich Castle Museum, proved to be of an uncommon species, ***Meta bourneti***, differing from its commoner relative in certain small but distinctive details of structure.

One other example had been identified from a Suffolk locality previously and this year, according to the November issue of the British Arachnological Society's newsletter, others have been discovered in Hertfordshire, Gloucestershire and at Puffin Island off Anglesey, all from underground cavities.

Shortly afterwards, Mr J. Rolfe, of Thrandeston, near Diss, sent me a specimen from a hollow elm tree, where it was found lurking behind a mass of oyster fungus.

Gossamer Web of Orb-Weaver

13/10/62

Autumn mists reveal the beauty of gossamer everywhere when we go out in the mornings. Delicate, close-woven sheets and tents are spread over the grass and between the forking branches of every bush and tree. Awesome funnel-shaped lairs are visible in the hollows of wayside banks and the depths of gorse bushes and even the bare earth of ploughlands often appears silvery with the drifting lifelines of countless spider aeronauts newly descended at the close of a fine day.

The webs exciting the greatest wonder are those constructed by the orb-weavers, typified by the plump, brown marbled garden spider (*Araneus diadematus*), with a glittering cross on her back. Her web may be a foot across at this season, like a silver net, constructed on a perfect geometrical pattern, with radiating lines and spirals joining them. Why this particular spider thrives best in gardens I do not know, but it may be because there is just that little extra shelter and warmth which makes a critical difference to the creature's chance of survival in autumn, when the female reaches maturity and lays her eggs in pale silken cocoons.

Some other closely related orb-weavers live mainly in reed beds, others on commons covered with gorse and brambles and yet others in bushy places and orchards. All are richly coloured, with cryptic patterns on their bodies and all reach full size in late summer or autumn.

The webs are spun at night as a rule, but on a calm evening in summer the work may begin before sunset, so that it is possible to see what happens. Webs, for all their intricate beauty, seldom last for more than two or three days, and they can be ruined very speedily by wind and rain coming together.

The spinning of a new one does not take very long. First a main bridging line is stretched between two supports and made strong by the joining of several silken strands. Next the foundation of the web pattern is laid elaborated with numerous radiating "spokes".

Having fixed the "woof", the spider goes to the centre and quickly moves in widening circles, fixing the "weft" in place. She then works back towards the middle adding a further series of threads which this time are provided with drops of a sticky fluid calculated to ensnare insects. The spider then sits either in the middle of the web or at the end of a sensitive line close by and waits until flies begin to struggle. She darts forward, rolls her victims in silk and takes them to a convenient spot where she may fed on them, before discarding the remains.

The male orb-weavers are smaller than their wives and make smaller webs. When the time comes for mating, these husbands show signs of great nervousness and pay many, very brief, running visits to their spouses during which the fertilising elements are literally handed over almost like pinches of snuff.

It is not unusual for the female to seize and devour her husband in the end, and this he seems to know in advance.

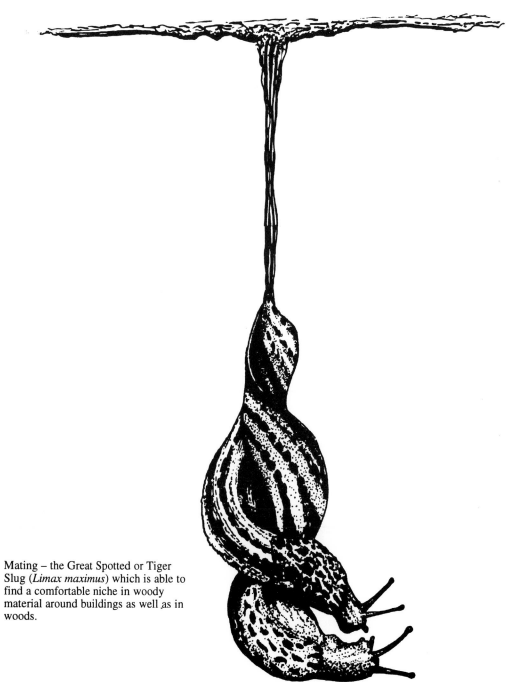

Mating – the Great Spotted or Tiger
Slug (*Limax maximus*) which is able to
find a comfortable niche in woody
material around buildings as well as in
woods.

Slug Homes in on Rotting Wood

14/4/84

The Great Spotted or Tiger Slug (**Limax maximus**) flourishes chiefly in our woods, but also finds many a comfortable niche wherever woody material in rotten condition is available in the neighbourhood of buildings.

One can often find it in yards where logs are stacked and near rubbish heaps in gardens, creeping forth at night to browse on moulds and larger fungi or on garbage and rotting vegetation.

Happily it does not attack living green plants and therefore does not menace crops of field or garden, which is just as well, sinceit is quite a monster attaining a length of up to 20cm.

I have known one large individual to consume the greater part of a sizeable toadstool for its supper. By day, these creatures retire under logs and loose bark or in other dark damp recesses, sometimes several huddling together. They vary in colour and marking, but are most commonly greyish with a tinge of purple-brown, and boldly striped and spotted with dark brown.

On mild summer nights mating couples can be found entwined like snakes as they dangle from a thread of thick slime from a tree branch, twirling about in this fashion for several hours.

Later, clusters of eggs are secreted in crevices of rotten tree stumps or leaf mould. The pale grey young come forth at the approach of spring and take three or four years to reach maximum size. Their keen sense of smell leads them to the fungi which they most relish and they are capable of travelling a hundred yards on their nocturnal forays when they get wind of something tasty in the offing; but it is their habit to return to their regular roosts before dawn.

I have found them eating dry rot fungus in buildings and although this might be thought helpful, one has to remember that the fungi make use of these slugs for disseminating their spores. The very glutinous slime of these slugs serves to discourage birds and other creatures from eating them, but no doubt they are often snapped up by predators while still young and relatively defenceless in this respect.

Elusive Slayer that Preys on Earthworms

13/8/55

Those who are unexpectedly late on a soft summer's night are sometimes rewarded by a glimpse of strange small creatures quite as surprising as leprechauns and elves stealing about their nocturnal business in the garden.

The luminous centipede, travelling below, might be taken for Oberon's royal train. The gauzy lacewing, fiery-eyed, might be Titania herself, caught fleetingly in the beam of a torch. Woodlice move like armour-plated beasts of the ancient world, now lilliputian, with winged dragon-earwigs and coal-black devil's coach-horse beetles of a fiercer mien. In the quiet and the dew, earthworms make holiday, lying out of their burrows in luscious ease.

It is at such a time that one of night's most extraordinary beings stalks abroad, dealing silent death. Few people ever see this elusive slayer in action and do not know that it lives in their gardens, because it is apt to be overlooked as but one of many kinds of slug. It is called the Shelled Slug because it has a slug-like form and carries an inconspicuous little shell near its tail; but it is not a true slug and ceases to look like one when it is at the height of a ferocious attack upon its prey.

Stealing upon a dew-happy worm, it opens a horrible round mouth and shoots out a long tongue covered with sharp barbed teeth, which lacerate and hold the victim in a shark's grip. If the worm happens to have its tail-tip still in the ground, there is a convulsive retreat and the attacker is whisked down the hole out of sight, still holding fast to its prey.

There is no escape for the worm that way, however. Very soon the head is gulped into the slug's muscular mouth, which is able to master the pull of even the most powerful lobworm in its death throes. As with the heron swallowing a large eel, digestion is begun very quickly and in time the tail of the victim disappears.

A Shelled Slug becomes oddly distorted and torpid after a big meal, like the python which swallowed a goat. It does not confine its attentions to worms; true slugs and centipedes are said to be eaten occasionally.

By day it hides in its own underground tunnel, lined with tough slime and in winter the creature makes a kind of cocoon deep in the earth. It has been known to live as much as six years, which is a great span for a land mollusc. Even as an infant it feeds on tiny worms, its prey increasing in size with its age and strength.

Centipedes Lit Up

Norwich 19/3/83

A friend wandering though an oak wood to the south of Norwich at night was surprised to see green lights flashing among the dead leaves under foot when these were disturbed. I think that there can be no doubt that the phosphorescent sparkle came from luminous centipedes (***Geophilus carpophagus***), which have often been taken for glow-worms displaying out of season.

They are to be found chiefly in old deciduous woods which have thick leaf carpets and rotten stumps in them and they are most likely to be noticed from autumn to the early spring when the undergrowth tends to be well moistened, since centipedes require a damp atmosphere when pursuing activities above ground.

Unlike glow-worms, they exude luminous fluid in droplets when disturbed, scattering them so that they have the effect of confusing would-be predators. Curiously enough, these creatures are blind and it is therefore strange that they should behave in this way, although it has been suggested that they may have some measure of sensitivity to light in the absence of eyes.

They have reddish-brown bodies up to three inches long and about a hundred legs.

They prey on other small inhabitants of the undergrowth and have been known to wander into damp buildings at night, helping to rid them of noxious insects. They have been known to hunt and destroy bed bugs when these were common in town and country houses up to the end of the 19th century.

The centipedes abound in some damp woods, but tend to be rare or absent in drier ones. A few years ago, following the clearance of one of their favourite habitats, hundreds swarmed into a neighbouring cottage, greatly alarming the occupants. Two other British centipedes are known to be luminous. One of these a long, slender, yellowish-brown species (***Haplophilus subterraneus***) lives underground, and is occasionally seen wrapped spirally round an earthworm struggling in its death throes at the surface.

This was witnessed on one occasion in the grounds of Norwich Castle. I have not yet encountered the remaining "fire-flasher", a red species (***Strigamia crassipes***) in Norfolk.

Visit of Nocturnal Millipedes

Brundall 2/2/65

Some years ago, when I lived at Brundall, I once woke up in the middle of the night to find hundreds of very strange little animals creeping over the bedroom ceiling. They were scarcely an eighth of an inch long and travelled at an almost imperceptibly slow and even pace, pausing from time to time presumably to feed on minute and virtually invisible plaster-moulds which were endeavouring to grow on the slightly damp ceiling.

This I found was the case on making careful inspection the following day, by which time the small crawlers had vanished. These nocturnal visitors were millipedes, *Polyxenus lagurus*.

When illuminated by electric light they appeared golden and furry, with cockade-like silken tails and glittering brush-like tufts along their sides unlike the armour-plated and rather snake-like millipedes one sees in leaf mould under trees; they look more like minute "woolly-bear" caterpillars.

It may be that their peculiar bristles help to prevent their small bodies from becoming shrivelled up in the dry air when they venture forth, and at other times save them from drowning when they happen to be drenched by rain in some of their more open habitats.

Normally, one finds them hiding under stones or under bark on tree trunks during the day. I have also come across them browsing on moulds and lichens on old stumps and gateposts at night, and under driftwood on Scolt Island, and they have even been found living unharmed in the large pine-needle nests of red forest ants, where again they are able to feed on fungi.

In the northern part of their range in Europe, these millipedes reproduce themselves parthenogenetically; the females breed without the participation of males, as do the stick-insects commonly kept as curious pets nowadays (1965). Thus a colony can be built up very rapidly, starting with a single parent.

Males are present in the south of Europe, but we do not know if any are present in British localities.

Cluster Fly's Response to Spring

Norfolk 4/4/59

Every year, at daffodil time, a little after the first butterflies have shaken off the sloth of winter and spread their flashing wings in the early sunshine, there comes a morning of gentle warmth and promise which brings forth legions of insects all of a sudden. Many of these have been lurking in leafy litter under evergreens, hedge-bottoms and flood refuse: some have been hiding under loose bark or in hollow trees, while a few have been willing prisoners in buildings during the dead months.

Chief among the species in the last category is the cluster fly (***Pollenia rudis)***, and it is the only British insect which regularly hibernates in attics, barns and churches in really large numbers, although swarms of some very much smaller flies seek similar shelter here and there. It is like a slightly smaller edition of the common bluebottle and the forepart or thorax is clothed with shining, pale golden hairs. The abdomen appears more grey than black, because of the number of little square mirror-like facets on its surface; but there is a well-marked black dividing line running down the middle of the back.

Cluster flies have the habit of massing in corners of roofs almost like swarms of bees in the depths of winter. Round about Easter-tide they begin to crawl and flop about clumsily, when it is not uncommon for them to prove embarrassing to churchgoers. After they have shaken off this dangerous drowsiness and reached the open air, they take every opportunity to bask in the sunshine, on walls, tree trunks and gateposts while spring gets under way.

Although they do not again become massed in crawling heaps, they continue to assemble in fairly large numbers, so that one may see a group of them covering as much as the area of a dinner plate on a tree trunk. Later, they visit flowers, especially those of umbelliferous plants such as hedge parsley and, having built up their strength and vitality, they proceed to mate and lay eggs in the ground, where earthworms are likely to be most abundant.

The maggots in due course seek out the worms and enter their bodies. Before settling down to consume their victims, they perform a little operation which ensures that they shall have a channel to the outside for breathing purposes. Then the worms are eaten from within, with such nice precision and deliberation that they continue to lead almost normal lives until the end. The maggots pupate in the ground and after varying periods, according to prevailing soil temperatures, the cluster flies emerge.

I would say that these insects tend to be most plentiful in the vicinity of houses and farms where earthworms are encouraged by the regular manuring of the cultivated ground. It should be added that these flies do not find any household foods attractive, so they are not a source of contamination.

Agate Snail and its Life Underground

Brampton, Norfolk 30/1/54

Much interest is taken in the peculiar creatures which live at great depths in the earth, in caves, underground rivers and subterranean lakes. These, like certain animals from the dark ocean depths, are for the most part white and blind.Some of them have near relatives which live in more normal surroundings and have pigmented bodies and properly developed eyes; but there are others whose ancestors sought refuge in the darkness of caverns when outside conditions proved wholly disastrous to all the rest of their tribe, and these may be regarded as living fossils.

As I have said, zoologists very naturally devoted much attention to such relict forms. Oddly enough, little study appears to have been given to the life of a very common subterranean creature of the English soil, namely the little agate snail which is both white and blind and yet lives only a few feet underground. I was shown some of these snails after they had been found buried in a Roman pot at Brampton the other day. Others turned up in Saxon pots excavated at Thetford a few years ago. I have seen them mingled with calcined bones in Bronze Age cremation urns.

I removed half a dozen from the inside of a human skull dug up at Caister on Sea, next to Great Yarmouth, on one occasion; others were associated with buried bones of domestic animals, including pig, on an Iron Age site at Postwick in 1935. Indeed, archaeologists are more familiar with these snails than naturalists in this part of the country.

What agate snails eat does not seem to be known with any certainty. It has been suggested by some authorities that they feed on rootlets in the soil and by others that they are carnivorous. The form of the shell mouth and the teeth has features in common with those of the predatory dog whelks found in the sea. They are often found in places where no roots are present, but at the same time there is no evidence that they attack other subterranean animals. Their common association with limy material and old bones suggests that they may obtain their food from these, possibly in the form of derivatives altered and enriched by the action of microscopic soil organisms.

It is of local interest that the first agate snails noticed in Norfolk were found by J B Bridgman, a Norwich dental surgeon, in the loose earth between stones on the bank "near the Thorpe toll-bar" about ninety years ago.

The agate snail is rather less than a quarter of an inch long. Its white body may be studied while the creature is alive, for it shows up perfectly through the shining, translucent shell. It is particularly interesting to observe the pulsation of the breathing organ under a low magnification.

False Scorpions "Thumb A Lift" on Horse-Flies

14/11/70

We have about 26 kinds of false scorpions in Britain, but they are so very small, only a few millimetres in length, very few people ever notice them.

They tend to move slowly in a crab-like manner, waving their pincers gently as they go. Unlike true scorpions they have no long jointed stinging tail to curl up threateningly when they are disturbed.

Several species live in woodlands where they creep under loose bark of rotting sticks and boughs on the ground. A few inhabit seashores between tidemarks and one of the largest (*Dactylochelifer latreillei)* is to be found commonly under driftwood at various places along the Norfolk coast.

I have come across "household" species on the walls and ceilings of cellars, including the dungeons under the keep of Norwich Castle; these are blind creatures which probably used to inhabit caves. Vision is poor in most of the false scorpions and they rely largely on feeling their way around with the help of tactile bristles.

From time to time one finds them attached to house flies and less frequently to other insects, including grasshoppers. They are not parasites, however, and do no damage to their hosts. Their purpose in clinging to these insects is to make use of them as a means of transport; they are in fact true hitch-hikers.

When house flies are emerging from manure heaps where many of them breed, they stay to sun themselves while their wings are drying and it is during this time that the false scorpions creep forth from the litter and hang on to their legs and bristles.

As like as not the flies will soon find their way into a building and settle on the wall indoors and then the hikers slip away and hide in the crevices. At night they steal out of their niches to hunt for small mites and "book-lice" which breed commonly in the damper parts of houses.

Presumably they obtain "lifts" in the opposite direction ocasionally, when the flies go off to heaps of manure to breed in summer, and there is no lack of mites for them to eat in the moist litter. However, it pays the hikers to seek warmer quarters indoors for part of the year, although some species remain active outside all the year round.

Wine-Flies Have Revealed Deep Secrets

Norfolk 14/12/63

If you have a dish of ripe fruit on the table, you will very likely see small flies making a bee-line for it sooner or later. These make their approach in slow motion, seeming almost to creep through the air and when they alight, they crawl with the same deliberate action. Similar flies haunt waste-bins in kitchens; they are always in close attendance whenever home-made wines are being prepared; they crawl into empty beer and milk bottles and are attractedbyvinegar; you will also see them hovering around rotten fruit in orchards and clustering on the sap that oozes from trunks of failing trees. They breed in fermenting juices; this is why fruity and alcoholic scents attract them.

About 25 species of these "wine flies" or "vinegar flies" (***Drosophila***) have been found in this country and several of them appear in all parts of the world where people eat fruit. They tend to be specially plentiful in towns because they have so many opportunities for breeding in garbage.

If you want to study them, you can always trap plenty of them, probably of several species, in a matter of a few hours, simply by putting some squashed banana out in the garden, as a bait.

At a suitable temperature, these flies breed faster than any other insects. A new generation of flies can be produced within a week or ten days of the eggs being laid. Because of this very convenient habit ***Drosophila*** has been used more than any other animal for studies in genetics. It has very large chromosomes and these have received more attention than those of any other creature by biologists investigating the intricate mechanisms of inheritance. By controlled and extensive inbreeding, many remarkable mutant forms of these insects have been established and used for experiments.

Normally, true flies have two proper wings and two little flipper scales called halteres in place of extra wings. Specimens of ***Drosophila*** carrying four wings have been produced; others have two very short wings or no wings at all. Variation occurs in many other features of their anatomy and the geneticists have separated and combined these characteristics at will in order to discover more about the behaviour of genes which are linked in the chromosomes. Our little "wine-flies" have revealed many of the deepest secrets of the living world to science.

Ivy Spread by Migrant Birds

24/1/70

The common and much maligned ivy is a plant of very great interest and significance.

Stemming from the brood of ***Araliaceae*** centred in the Philippines region, its generic stock has become established over most of Asia and Europe and the Mediterranean coast of North Africa through the agency of birds.

It owes much to its liberation by birds of the thrush family wintering in the south and feeding on the berries during their northward migrations in spring. Digesting the fruit pulp and dropping the pips under trees and among rocks, the migrants have gradually carried the ivy right up to the Arctic Circle as well as to the outlying islands and mountain heights.

The ripening of the berries at the very end of winter has made this possible. Flowering occurs in early autumn, when the gold-green umbels provide abundant nectar for vast numbers of insects while there is little competition from other plants for their interest, the result being that most of the blossoms seed.

Ivy climbs rocks and tree trunks with the help of small, whiskery, adhesive roots put forth in early summer. These soon die and shrink pulling the stems closer to their supports. They are not designed for imbibing nourishment as the plant is not parasitic.

The foliage of the climbing shoots is jagged and very variable in outline; that accompanying the flowering shoots is narrower and more streamlined, allowing light and air to circulate freely, with clear access for visitors to the flowers and berries in season. In woodland shade one finds sterile forms carpeting the ground and trees are climbed mainly where they are open to the light at least on one side.

Ivy has little success in mounting the trunks of trees which have a thick leaf canopy, such as beeches and conifers. It thrives on old wayside oaks which are failing or dead and it is often falsely blamed for their ruin.

However, it can be harmful to young trees by robbing them of light with its leafy bowers. So its spread should be controlled in young plantations, while on ancient trees on the whole it can be safely left unmolested to enhance the beauty of the countryside and provide sustenance for bees, butterflies and birds.

Ivy gives good protection with its tile-like leaves on the walls of houses, but it must not be allowed to force its way under the tiles; with judicious pruning at the top, it is a great asset and might be used much more than it is for hiding ugly buildings.